Praise for *The Reluctant Caregiver*

"The Reluctant Caregiver *is an honest and intimate look into the caregiver's perspective of brain injury and it should be a must read for every rehab professional. I have more understanding and compassion for what a caregiver goes through, which will help me better support patients and their loved ones on their rehabilitation journeys."* **—Ashlea Walter, BCom, MScOT, Occupational Therapist**

"This book's topic is emotionally intense, but the writing style is clear and vulnerable and heartwarming, which creates a safe landing place for the reader. The result is a gripping memoir about the advantages of choosing self-care, even when it rocks our closest relationships." **—Grace Kerina, author of *Personal Boundaries for Highly Sensitive People***

"I am a caregiver, professionally and personally, and I work with, and support parents, teachers, doctors, first responders, and therapists. Devon Ervin's tender, poignant and accessible memoir, The Reluctant Caregiver, was written for us. More than once while absorbed in the book I found hard to put down, I found myself thinking, 'how did she do this?' and yet she does work valiantly to try to make normal, a life that is anything but." **—Marilyn Finch Williams, LCSW, Psychotherapist and Coach, primarily serving professional caretakers**

"Reading Devon Ervin's The Reluctant Caregiver: Reclaiming My Life After Caring for a Stroke Survivor *feels like having a heart-to-heart with a close friend who's come through the fire stronger than ever. Honest, vulnerable, and relatable, it's a must-read for anyone feeling the weight of caregiving. I wish I'd had this book during my own journey. Let Devon's touching stories remind you that healing can come in many ways."* **—Maya Bairey, author of *Painting Celia***

"Having had the privilege of watching this brave and important book come to be, I am thrilled to see it out in the world as a beacon of light to others who may suddenly find themselves in the role of a reluctant caregiver." **—Sulima Malzin, author of *Arms Filled With Bittersweet***

"Devon Ervin chooses her words with the precision of a poet. Words which took me along in the ambulance; kept me on the edge of my seat while potential life sustaining medical decisions by dedicated doctors seemed based on the flip of a coin; and gave me a place in the support groups while the couple gave back to the community of stroke survivors and families. What surprises me is that my lingering thoughts are of a yearning to have a relationship like they had built before the stroke; and the utmost respect for where they have taken their family, over time." **—Kay DeLay, writer, caregiver, avid reader**

"Devon Ervin writes with an honest and intimate voice that allows us to experience her young husband's baffling stroke, the labyrinth of medical intervention, and loving transformation of their marriage. Read this book to understand what a stroke is, what it can do to a brilliant mind, why it transforms identity, and how it can reconnect a woman to her self. Through these pages, you can watch her grow and find yourself cheering for her through tears." **—Chrissa Kruger, daughter-in-law of stroke survivor**

"A beautifully woven story of love, self-sacrifice and the journey to healing the self, crafted in a way that feels authentic and relatable. Devon gives permission (not that it is needed) for others to care for themselves—whatever that looks like—after experiencing the loss of a partner as we knew them, in a gentle and loving way." **—Susan Johnson, former caregiver**

"This is a story of love, of losing and reclaiming "self", and of thoughtful and meaningful choices in the face of life events beyond one's control. Devon's story allows the reader to drop into her life experiences over a period of time and to witness her fear, her pain, her joy and her recovery. I have a new perspective and respect for caregivers everywhere." **—Friend of stroke survivor**

"You marry the love of your life, and everything is wonderful until suddenly, it's not. This is an honest and insightful telling of one woman's journey when her life is thrown into chaos after her partner has a stroke. I very much felt Devon's struggle as she is suddenly thrown into the role of "caregiver" for her husband only to discover that he has become a different person. It's a story of love and loss as she struggles with difficult choices, a man she no longer knows, and fights to reclaim her own identity. It was a thought-provoking read and one that I'll recommend for my book club." **—Friend of stroke survivor**

THE RELUCTANT CAREGIVER

Reclaiming My Life After Caring for a Stroke Survivor

A Memoir

Devon Ervin

TheReluctantCaregiverBook.com

HIGHPOINT

Excerpt(s) from *GIFT FROM THE SEA* by Anne Morrow Lindbergh, copyright © 1955, 1975, copyright renewed 1983 by Anne Morrow Lindbergh. Used by permission of Pantheon Books, an imprint of the Knopf Doubleday Publishing Group, a division of Penguin Random House LLC. All rights reserved.

This edition published by Highpoint Life Books
For information, write to info@highpointpubs.com.

First Edition
ISBN: 979-8-9879203-3-6

Library of Congress Cataloging-in-Publication Data

Ervin, Devon
The Reluctant Caregiver
Reclaiming My Life After Caring for a Stroke Survivor
A Memoir

Summary: "Certified Life Coach Devon Ervin offers a collection of stories and poems about the days, months, and years following her husband's brain injuries and how those moments impacted her, their marriage, and their family. It walks the reader through a harrowing journey as Ervin finds her way back to being the author of her own life."
– Provided by publisher.

ISBN: 979-8-9879203-3-6 (Paperback)
1.Strokes 2. Memoir 3.Caregiving

Library of Congress Control Number: 2023908795

Cover and Interior Design by Sarah M. Clarehart

Manufactured in the United States of America

Note from the Author

This is my story, as told through my memory, my lens, my truth.
My story clearly intersects with the stories of others and
I acknowledge and honor that all of our stories are valid,
even if remembered differently or not at all.
My only claim is that I am sharing my story
as I remember experiencing it.

For my beloved daughters.
May you never lose yourselves
as you care for others.

Contents

Prologue

When asked how we met, Tim would always chuckle and say we met in a bar. I would give him a look of mock exasperation and say we were always destined to meet. He'd smile and wait for me to tell the rest of the story. Yes, we technically met in a bar, but not *that* kind of bar.

It was the early '90s, I was in my late twenties, and we were both part of a large group of friends who met on Tuesday nights at a local brew pub for pizza and beer. It was a meetup before meetups were a thing. It started with a group of guys who worked in the tech industry who liked to brew their own beer. I didn't drink beer or brew it but was dating someone who did, so each Tuesday around dinnertime I found myself at a bar with an ever-expanding group of friends who showed up for food, beverages, and lively conversation.

Tim and I knew each other indirectly for a year or so before we actually spoke to one another. I knew he was an engineer. I knew he was divorced. He knew I was dating a guy he knew from a previous workplace. He knew my cousin. We had friends in common. We played flag football together with a large group. We had been circling around each other for years without even really noticing.

After my relationship with my boyfriend ended, Tim and I had our first real conversation at the brew pub on a Tuesday night. We clicked. We clicked so much that I got scared and stopped going to the brew pub on Tuesday nights. I knew I needed to heal my heart and do some inner work before I jumped into another relationship. After six months, I felt the urge to go back. I wanted to see Tim. I wanted to know if there was anything there. I wanted to take that great big step and, even though I was scared, I showed up.

We talked. We still clicked.

That night was the beginning of a beautiful relationship.

Four years later, we stood on a bluff on the island of St. Thomas reciting wedding vows to each other in front of four of our closest friends. It was magical and casual and beautiful and heartfelt, and a thousand rainbows all lit up with love. As part of our ceremony, we read personal letters to each other. (All these years later, I can still hear him reading these words.)

Devon –

The first thing I noticed about you was your quiet voice. I had to strain to hear you over the noise of our friends at the Bridge-port, but I'm glad I did. As I listened to you, I realized that your voice was soft, but your ideas and your wisdom were clear and strong.

Your convictions about the importance of spending time with the people we care about helped me change my life. I love you for many reasons—the beauty you have on the inside and the outside; the insight you have into people that always amazes me; the inner strength that you've drawn on to go back to school to build a life and career that truly fulfills you; and the genuine love and care you show toward your family and friends. But the most important reason may also be the most selfish—I know that I'm a better person with you in my life than I am without you.

My whole life is better with you in it. You make our house a home. Without you, it's brick and glass and wood (mostly green, but maybe a little gray). With you, it's a sanctuary—a place to renew myself; a place for us to share thoughts and love; a place to grow and learn to face the world tomorrow better than we did today.

I don't know what the future holds, but I know that there's no one I'd rather have by my side to travel into it with me than you. I'm looking forward to the journey. Thank you for sharing it with me.

I love you.

It was a magical time. He was a software engineer doing work he loved. I was a psychotherapist doing work I loved. Dual income, no kids. We traveled a lot. We spent a lot of time with friends. We focused on our careers and seeing the world and playing as much as possible. We shared inside jokes. We had a beautiful home in an old neighborhood, and we loved our lives. Our relationship wasn't perfect, but it was strong and solid and beautiful.

About a decade later, my biological clock unexpectedly kicked into overdrive and I found myself constantly thinking about raising a child. It wasn't necessarily a drive to give birth but more of a deep longing to raise a child. We had decided before we married that if we were to have children, it would be through adoption. For years we had both been on the fence about having kids. I felt a pull to adopt from an orphanage; Tim felt the pull to do his part to stop population growth. Adoption was a good fit for both of us, and yet, at the time of our marriage, neither one of us was ready to start a family. So all those years later I was a little surprised to find myself thinking about raising a child. I was emotional and overwhelmed and, frankly, a little afraid to bring it up. Tears would come to my eyes when I would think about it.

It was visceral and surprising, and I kept wondering how the hell I was going to bring it up with my husband.

One fall evening, a few months after my biological clock kicked in, we were having a lovely dinner in our favorite restaurant, a New Orleans–style bistro in the NE section of our city. We were sitting at the bar in a tiny little restaurant, talking, making plans for the holidays, and enjoying some amazing food. We were listening to jazz and soaking up the ambiance in that beautiful space. The conversation meandered to gift ideas for friends and family. When trying to think of something to get for his parents, Tim said they'd really be happy if we had a baby. He may have been a little drunk and may have been half-joking, but I was flooded with emotion and started crying. I told him what I wanted; how I wanted to raise a child. I wanted that experience. I believed he and I would be great parents. He was stunned and a little quiet. I wiped my tears and asked him to please think about it and he agreed to do so.

After a couple of months of processing, he let me know he also felt ready to raise a child. I can still remember in vivid detail the moment when he shared that news. We were so excited, so over the moon, so ready for the next phase in our lives together. We took the plunge and started the long road toward adoption. We dove into the process headfirst—choosing an agency, taking classes, reading books, telling our families and friends, and making changes in our home. We were going to create a family.

We were connected.

We were happy.

We were living our happily-ever-after love story.

PART ONE

The Sneaker Wave

When you love someone you do not love them
all the time, in exactly the same way,
from moment to moment. It is an impossibility.
It is even a lie to pretend to.
And yet this is exactly what most of us demand.
We have so little faith in
the ebb and flow of life, of love,
of relationships. We leap at the flow
of the tide and resist in terror its ebb.
We are afraid it will never return.

— Anne Morrow Lindbergh

Insomnia
Late January 2008

It's three in the morning on a random Thursday and, as usual, I can't sleep. *Damned insomnia*. I grab my book, flip on the book light and start reading, hoping the distraction will relax me. My husband gets up and walks down the short hallway to the bathroom. When he comes back to bed a few minutes later, I do my best to elicit some sympathy.

"I can't sleep," I say in my most whiny voice.

He laughs and responds by asking if he can rub my hands, something he does to help me relax. It's a sweet routine that happens often: he massages my hands, he relaxes, he falls asleep, and I go back to reading. This time is no exception. *Damned insomnia*.

I hear him cough. It's a weird, deep, guttural cough that strikes me as odd, as he's not sick and rarely coughs. With my back to him, I ask if he's okay. He doesn't respond. I turn to face him and again ask if he's okay. He's looking at me, but his face remains passive. I'm confused and a little irritated at this point. I wonder why he's avoiding the question and wonder if I've somehow pissed him off. I ask the question again, this time louder and with more urgency. His eyes are open and he's looking at me, but his lips are closed, and he looks like he's smirking. What the bloody hell?

The panic starts. I yell at him to answer me. No response. I throw off the covers, jump out of bed, and run to flip on the overhead light. I'm standing over him yelling at him to answer me. I'm so confused. He's using his left hand to lift his right arm off the bed as if his right arm is asleep. I wonder how his arm can be asleep. I'm not connecting his lack of speech to the issue with his arm. I beg him to talk to me. I threaten to call 911 if he doesn't. He just looks at me blankly and again seems interested in his right arm.

I reach for the landline phone on the nightstand on his side of the bed. He uses his left arm to force the phone back down to the receiver. The panic explodes in me. I scream at him to answer me *right now* or I'm calling 911. No response.

My hand is visibly shaking as I make the call. The 911 operator answers and I blurt out, "My husband won't talk to me." As the words come out of my mouth, I realize how absurd they sound. I wonder if the operator thinks we're fighting. I wonder if it's possible that Tim is giving me the silent treatment. I'm so confused and have no idea what is happening. I describe the situation and answer the questions as best I can.

The operator asks if Tim's face is drooping. I stare at Tim and tell the operator he looks normal but his expression is kind of flat. The operator says, "Your husband may be having a stroke." I'm really confused now. *A stroke? This must be a mistake. Tim is the healthiest person I know. He's in his 40s. Only old people have strokes. What's a stroke? What does this mean? What do I do now?*

The operator calmly says an ambulance is on the way and offers to stay on the phone until they arrive. I decline, hanging up the phone to quickly get dressed. I run to the closet, throw on some clothes, and run to turn off the home alarm.

I'm putting on shoes when the paramedics knock on the door. I didn't think to unlock the door. I open the door and a flood of people in uniform come filing in. Paramedics, fire fighters, ambulance personnel. As I stand there holding the door, I notice it's dark and raining outside and the lights on both the fire truck and the ambulance are illuminating the entire neighborhood. I make sure the door gets securely closed so the cats won't get out. I am really shaking now.

I follow the paramedics to the bedroom and watch in disbelief as they surround the bed, asking questions, taking Tim's vital signs. His eyes are open, but he doesn't respond to *anything* and I find it odd that he doesn't seem distressed at all. He doesn't appear to be able to move his right side. They start him on oxygen. He's wearing blue and black plaid flannel pajama bottoms. That memory gets burned into my brain. It takes several of them to lift him as he is not able to help at all. They place him on a gurney and move toward the front door.

I grab Tim's wallet, my cell phone, a box of tissues, and my purse. I quickly set the house alarm and run down the driveway to the ambulance in the pouring rain, crying hysterically, clutching my box of tissues, praying for Tim, and thanking God over and over and over for my insomnia.

The Maiden Ambulance Voyage
January 2008 – Thirty Minutes After Stroke

I hoist myself up into the passenger seat of the ambulance, awkwardly clutching a box of tissues and my purse. I have never been in an ambulance. It reminds me a little of riding in a U-Haul truck—it has a different view than what is visible from my car. I can't see Tim. I consider turning around to look for him but don't want to take my eyes off the road.

It is still dark and raining and the lights of the ambulance are casting an eerie light show on the trees as we quickly travel the fifteen blocks to the hospital. I am lulled by the cadence of the windshield wipers and wonder why I don't hear the siren. Maybe the driver doesn't turn it on because there is no traffic at this hour in our neighborhood. Maybe I'm not hearing well. I'm not sure.

We pull into the bay behind the hospital and Tim is quickly unloaded and taken straight into the emergency room. I scramble out of the front of the vehicle to follow him, struggling a little as I misjudge the distance to the ground.

I am still somewhat hysterical as I close the ambulance door and move toward the hospital. I think it's only been a few minutes since we left home, but I'm not sure. Time is progressing quickly and slowly at irregular intervals. My sense of time is completely off. We enter the emergency room through the back door, throwing off my sense of place as well as my sense of time, making the whole experience that much more surreal. It all seems so random.

They rush (or maybe they slowly walk) my husband down a hallway to get a CT scan while I handle the paperwork for insurance and medical history. I am standing here, holding a giant box of tissues, crying, trying to focus, wondering what kind of wild ride we are on.

Prayers in the ER
January 2008 – One Hour After Stroke

Someone lightly taps me on the shoulder and tells me I have visitors. I am confused. *Visitors?* I am really struggling to comprehend what is happening.

Tim is still off getting his first CT scan as I am escorted to a small, private family waiting room next to the ER. I am surprised this room exists and I'm so relieved not to be in the large public waiting area as I had expected to be. I am still crying and clutching my box of tissues. I walk into the room and see my mom and her husband sitting there waiting for me. My mom is visibly distressed and crying. My mom's husband looks a little shocked but, as usual, shows little emotion.

I don't want to be here. I don't want to console my mom. I don't want her to console me. I just want answers. I just want to be near Tim. I glance repeatedly at the door and wonder when I can get out of here and go back to his room in the emergency room.

My mom hugs me, grabs my hand, and says we should pray. I feel myself pull away, surprised by the hot anger that floods through me. I immediately feel guilty. My heart knows she is being kind and loving and doing what she can, but I don't want this right now. I don't want to pray to her version of God. I feel disrespected and alone and so confused. I wonder if it even helps to pray for someone who is an atheist. I don't want to be polite and *good* right now. I just want to go back out there and find out what the fuck is happening to my husband.

I take a deep breath and tell them I need to go wait for Tim. I have to get back to Tim. I feel like a total bitch as I ask my mom to please feed our cats. I quickly hug her, take my box of tissues, and practically run out the door, back to the ER, back to the hell that is waiting there, wondering if I will be punished by some God for being mean to my mom.

A Game of Chance
January 2008 – Two Hours After Stroke

After what seems like hours but is likely just a few minutes in the waiting room with my mom and her husband, I am directed back to Tim's room in the ER and am surprised to see Tim is already there. My sense of time must be completely broken.

The doctor reports that the CT scan shows a large blood clot. It isn't a bleeding stroke, which apparently is good news, even though I am struggling to see how Tim being paralyzed and unable to speak can be considered good. My husband has been given a drug to break up the clot. I am confused and the doctor goes on to explain that the drug acts like Drano does in plumbing. That helps break through some of the fog that I am experiencing and makes sense.

Unfortunately, the doctor goes on to say the Drano isn't working. *Oh shit.*

The neurologist calmly and slowly explains to me that there are two treatments for this type of stroke—the Drano and a surgery. Unfortunately, at this point in time it is not yet approved to do both treatments at the same time. *What?* The anger and confusion swirl in my head as I try to process this information. Two treatments. One he's already had, which isn't working. The other is not available to him because it's not yet approved. *What the hell? Will they just let him die?*

I feel the heat rising in my body and notice a strong desire to scream and fight. I freeze instead. I may be holding my breath.

The doctor goes on to slowly explain that in order for Tim to have the surgery, he must participate in a study. Because he is unable to consent, I must choose whether or not to consent for him. I let out my breath and take another one. The doctor hands me a thick packet of papers to read. I can't focus. I can't think. I can't read. I wonder if I'm in shock. I am shaking and crying and confused as I stare at those pages and pages and pages of text. I am frantically flipping through the pages, not able to read or focus or take in anything.

The doctor calls my name and I lift my head to look at her. She calmly and directly tells me that his stroke was *large* and may be *fatal*. I hear her. I process this information. I hear myself say, "I don't know what to do."

She slowly tells me she can't decide for me.

I anxiously ask, "What would you do if he were your husband?" She quietly says she would consent to the surgery and then repeats that I am still the one who needs to make the decision.

I breathe deeply, and quietly say, "Yes."

She tells me they have to flip a coin to see if he will be a subject or a control in the study and leaves the room, taking all of the air in the world out the door with her. I stand alone in that semi-lit, eerily quiet emergency room wondering if my husband is going to survive if they say no. I wonder if I am going to survive if they say no. I even consider how I will hurt them if they say no. The helplessness. The powerless-ness. The bubbling rage. It's all there. Hope joins me for a brief moment and then is crushed a second later.

They flip the coin in another room.

He's in. He's in the study as a subject.

I exhale loudly, unaware I had been holding my breath.

Now, more than a decade later, I still wonder how many times they flipped that coin. Did they defy the odds in order to save his life? Best two out of three? If so, God bless them.

A Traumatic Ambulance Ride
January 2008 – Three Hours After Stroke

After a few traumatic hours at the hospital, Tim is being transferred. After testing, a diagnosis, and some unsuccessful treatment, he is being loaded back into an ambulance to go to another hospital for surgery. I'm not sure if it's the same ambulance we were in before or if it's the same driver. My memory has blurred those kinds of details. I hoist myself back up into the passenger seat, still clutching my box of tissues as if it is a beloved stuffed animal. I breathe a sigh of relief. I am now an experienced ambulance rider. I can handle this.

I'm wrong.

I can't handle this.

Nothing has prepared me for this ride in this ambulance on this freeway in this rush hour traffic before sunrise on this cold January morning.

As I float in and out of shock, I am acutely aware of the insanity that is happening on the freeway. Here we are in a large, boxy ambulance with sirens blaring and lights flashing, and cars still don't get out of the way. The heroic driver keeps getting on his loudspeaker and telling drivers to move over. Over and over: "Move over." We are driving in the rain, in the dark, at the beginning of rush hour. The ambulance is in the middle lane, allowing cars to move easily to the right or left and yet, at times, it's as if this giant, noisy, flashing vehicle is completely invisible. I wonder how drivers can't see or hear us. My head wants to explode. My body is hot and rigid, and I keep trying to focus on breathing. Sirens, windshield wipers, breathe. Lights flashing, cars less than a foot in front of us, breathe. Driver calmly shouting into the loudspeaker, "Move over," breathe. Ambulance weaving, me clutching my box of tissues, breathing, and breathing, and breathing as hot tears spill down my cheeks.

The distance from one hospital to the next is only about seven miles, but it requires us to cross the Willamette River and go through part of downtown. Basically, we are traveling from a NE portion of Portland, Oregon, to a SW portion. It is typically a twenty- or thirty-minute drive on a good day, longer if there is traffic. Since I am not tracking time well, I experience time as dragging and skipping all at the same time. I hold on for dear life as we fly around the curves up the hill to the hospital. I wonder why I don't remember crossing the bridge.

Tim is lying on his back on a gurney with his feet to the back of the ambulance. The road to the hospital on the hill is well known for its long and winding switchbacks. The perfect cocktail for motion sickness. I experience a slice of hell in the front of the vehicle, certain we will slide off the cliff. Meanwhile, Tim is in the back of the ambulance vomiting as we rush up the curvy road to the hope on the hill.

We arrive at the hospital just as the sun is starting to rise. The onset of dawn has changed the lighting but not the surreal nature of what is happening. It is still cold and raining and the rain is starting to turn to snow.

I slowly climb down out of the ambulance, still feeling wobbly and suspended from reality. I follow as Tim is wheeled into the emergency room, which is surprisingly dark and quiet. I take deep gulps of air, promising myself over and over that I will never, ever willingly climb back into an ambulance again.

It's been many years since that morning and I still have flash-backs from that drive. Sometimes as I feel my body start to react to the sound of sirens or the movement of fast-moving vehicles, I can breathe through the echoes of trauma. Sometimes I can't. Sometimes I must pull the car over and breathe. Sometimes

I must ask whoever is driving to slow down and keep some distance from the car in front of them. Sometimes I feel myself reach for my box of tissues, willing the wild-eyed panic that sits right there in my chest to settle down and breathe.

A Pat on the Back
January 2008 – Four Hours After Stroke

I stand beside Tim in a dimly lit emergency room and anxiously wait for the neurosurgeon to arrive. The room is dark and strangely quiet and we are taking up space in an aisle next to an empty nurses' station. I feel far too conspicuous and wish we were in a closed room.

The sun is starting to come up, flooding the area near the windows with light as the rest of the room remains dark and shadowy. This only adds to the surreal nature of the experience. We have this unexpected moment to breathe after several hours of frenzied activity. It's just me and Tim. He's lying on a gurney as I stand next to him, still clutching my box of tissues, and weeping silently while trying to hold it all together for him.

Tim reaches up with his left hand, the one not paralyzed, and pats me on the shoulder. I take his hand, feeling the love and comfort coming from him. We remain like that until they come to whisk him off to surgery.

I didn't know it then, but now, looking back, I see it was the passing of the torch. In those brief few minutes, our worlds flipped upside down and we shifted roles. We shifted from mutually caring for each other to me taking care of him, all in that one small, gut-wrenching gesture.

Clothing Choices
January 2008 – Four Hours After Stroke

I switch positions but still can't get comfortable in this stupid office-style chair. I am alone in a small hospital waiting room, quietly crying, wishing I had a blanket. My husband has just gone into the operating room and it is unknown how long his procedure will take. Someone is supposed to give me a briefing as soon as the surgery is over. I'm an exhausted, anxious mess.

I look down at the tissue box in my lap. I set it aside and realize I forgot to put on a bra after calling 911. *Oh God.* I instantly feel self-conscious, adding yet another unpleasant emotion to my experience. I'm wearing jeans with a white, long-sleeved t-shirt, and a fleece jacket with a small Mariner's logo embroidered on the front. The jacket is super soft and a beautiful shade of pink—not too light and not too dark. It fits me well and has become my favorite. I am really pissed at myself for not thinking to grab clothes that could be burned when this day is over. Why did I grab my favorite jacket? Why did I grab an article of clothing that had so many wonderful memories attached to it?

I remember buying the jacket. We were at a baseball game at Safeco Field in Seattle on a gorgeous fall day. It was a little chilly up in the stands, so I ventured to the gift shop to buy something to keep me a little warmer. Pink is not a color I wear often, so I was surprised when I saw the jacket and instantly loved it. I also bought a tiny, pink baseball cap for our future daughter, the daughter we hope to bring home from China sometime soon. Tim and I had taken the train up to Seattle for a long weekend. In addition to going to the baseball game, we poked around in Pike Place Market, walked around the city, and had long, meaningful conversations over fabulous meals in a variety of restaurants.

I startle when I hear the sound of a voice on the intercom in the hall of the hospital and the memory simply evaporates. I am back in the waiting room; back in my current nightmare.

Sadly, this pink jacket will now forever hold the memories of the trauma of this day—those that have happened already this morning and those that will unfurl over the next few hours, months, and years.

Damn.

I swear softly under my breath when I realize I also forgot to put on socks or grab a coat before running out the door to the ambulance earlier this morning. It is late January, snowing, and damned cold. Socks and a winter coat might have been good ideas. Then again, I would hate to want to burn a winter coat.

I sit here in this tiny waiting room, wondering if people should be encouraged to set aside clothes for emergencies, some that have no meaning at all—just as we do with food, water, candles, and flashlights. Disposable clothes for emergencies. Sounds reasonable to me.

I sigh heavily as I zip up my formerly favorite jacket as far as it will go. I shift positions once again and put the tissue box back on my lap, grateful to be holding something that can eventually easily be trashed.

Dreaded Phone Calls
January 2008 – Four Hours After Stroke

I stare at my phone and watch it become distorted as my eyes fill with tears. I'm sitting in the surgery waiting room, trying to imagine how I'm going to tell my in-laws that their son—their super-healthy, beloved son—has had a large stroke and is currently having surgery to remove a blood clot from an artery in his brain. I practice saying the words quietly to myself, hoping it will keep me from sobbing on the phone. I feel very, very alone.

I don't want to make the call and yet I know I must. I know it's the right thing to do, but I still don't want to make the call. I know I need support. I know Tim will need support. I just don't want to be the one to ask. I know I can't carry this pain alone and yet a part of me wonders if sharing this pain will actually reduce it or if it will simply make it less visible.

I scroll through my contacts looking for my father-in-law's name, take a deep breath, and start dialing. Tim's dad answers the phone and a few seconds later I hear his mom pick up the extension. This is the pattern. They exist as a unit. I won't have to share the story twice to them.

I hiccup and cry my way through the story. The pain in his mom's voice is visceral and heartbreaking. His mom cries and loudly says over and over, "Not Tim. Why couldn't it have been me?" This confuses me. I wouldn't want this to happen to her either. I realize she is probably talking to God, not to me, so I don't answer her. His dad asks several questions, which helps bring me back into the present moment. I let them know I will call them back as soon as Tim is out of surgery. No one asks how I am doing. It doesn't surprise me, but it hurts, nonetheless.

I hang up the phone and gather my thoughts and emotions again. The next call is to Chris. He is one of our best friends and also happens to currently be Tim's boss. They have known each other for a couple of decades and because they both work in the same field, their paths have crossed multiple times in job situations. At this moment Chris and his girlfriend (who just became his fiancée a couple of days ago) are on a skiing vacation in Canada. I am reluctant to make the call and interrupt Chris on vacation but know he will want to know, both personally and professionally. I make the call and tearfully walk through the story again. He listens. Without hesitation, he says they will get on a plane and be at the hospital as soon as humanly possible. I tearfully hang up the phone, feeling buoyed by a giant wave of relief.

The next call is to my work. I call the HR director and feel my armor go up as I tell the story. I have this weird belief that I must be strong and competent at all times. She is very supportive and kind and tells me not to worry about anything. I have absolutely no idea what is on my schedule for today or what tasks are left undone. I realize in this moment that none of it matters. The long days and the endless perfectionism and all the striving at my work mean absolutely nothing in the grand scheme of things. I have no space in my heart right now for guilt. It is what it is. I have no idea how long I will be gone and, honestly, it doesn't even matter. I wonder why I always thought it did.

My armor is still up as I call three more of Tim's closest friends and hear myself say yes when they ask if they can come to the hospital. I feel like a robot going through the motions and start making lists on a notepad I keep in my purse. The shift from feeling to doing helps pull me away from some of the shock and grief and panic that are lingering on the edge of my awareness.

Next I pick up the phone and call a few of my closest friends. They offer to come sit with me and I cry when a friend asks if I have eaten. Their concerns and questions surprise me. I am the nurturer. I am the giver. I am the one who takes care of everyone else. I am so incredibly scared and anxious and overwhelmed, but in this moment, I feel grateful to be able to call on my community for support. I feel the wagons circling, moving in to protect and comfort both of us.

I welcome the circling wagons.

A Picture Is Worth a Thousand Words
January 2008 – Five Hours After Stroke

The walls of this tiny surgical waiting room have never seen natural light. I am at the hospital, sitting in a pastel-colored room, anxiously waiting for someone to come and give me an update on my husband's surgery. This room is located in the middle of the building and there are no windows to the outside. As I wait, I wonder about the lack of natural light and how it impacts the waiting. I can't get comfortable. I stand up and stretch and move to a chair closer to the door so I can watch down the hall. The only window I see is in the door to the hallway and even that doesn't provide any natural light. I stare nervously out that window in the door, watching and waiting for news.

This room is like a cage, keeping me trapped as I wait for the doctor. I don't dare leave, even to go to the restroom. As I wait, another woman comes in. Now there are two of us in the cage. She is older, with gray hair and wrinkles. We share a knowing look. We are wives who sit for our husbands. We don't speak. We don't have to. The sadness, anxiety, and fear we are radiating speak volumes. We are both hoping and praying for miracles.

A while ago, the neurosurgeon assigned to Tim's case explained the procedure to me and then a nurse escorted me to this room to wait. I have no idea how long I have been waiting. Minutes feel like hours. The doctor said he hoped to remove the blood clot on the first try, but if he didn't, he would try several more times before giving up. That was comforting. I wouldn't want a surgeon who was a quitter.

I hear the door open and I look up to see the doctor. He is wearing scrubs and a little hat. He smiles broadly at me and I release the breath

I didn't know I was holding. He sits in the chair next to me and hands me two documents that look like x-rays. They are before and after photos of the blood flow in Tim's brain. The first one is unremarkable and the second one blows my mind. The blood flow is restored. I gasp. *Fuck*. How long would he have lived without blood to the majority of his brain? The doctor is talking to me, but I only hear snippets of what he is saying. "...retrieved the clot on the first try... surgery only took eleven minutes... took longer to prep and move him to recovery... he will go to the neuro-ICU... clot was very large... procedure went very well... you can see your husband soon..."

I continue to stare at the photos, flipping back and forth between the before and after shots and it finally dawns on me exactly what it means to have a stroke. Tears run down my cheeks as I thank the doctor profusely, thank him for handing me a miracle.

Now, looking back, I realize three miracles happened in those first four hours of that painful day. The first was me being awake when Tim's stroke happened, the second was getting into the research study that allowed for the surgery, and the third was the doctor who performed the procedure that ultimately saved my husband's life.

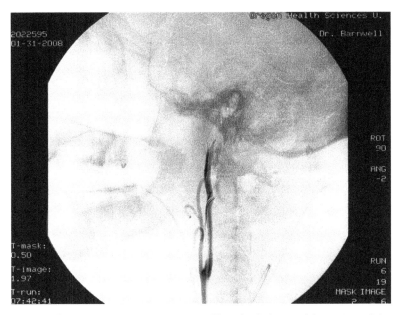

Photo of Tim's brain prior to surgery. The clot is located in center of the photo where the large artery from below seems to stop.

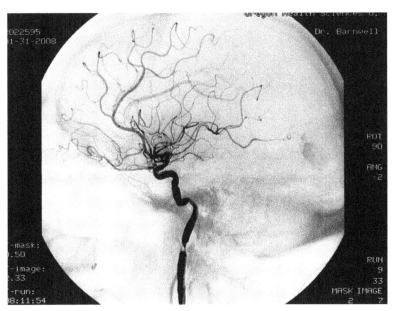

Photo of Tim's brain after surgery. Blood flow is restored.

Gray Skies
January 2008 – Eight Hours After Stroke

For the first time all day I am able to sit down and eat. Even though I haven't eaten since yesterday, I'm not really hungry. I sit mindlessly pushing my food around on my tray, wondering when my appetite will return. I am sitting on a stool at a counter in the hospital cafeteria, staring out the window. The counter by the window is cold and rather uninviting and I find myself strangely drawn to the view of the snowfall and the gray sky outside.

The window in front of me is quite large and offers a view that is surprisingly unobstructed. The rain has turned to snow and, except for the white flakes that are falling, everything is a dreary shade of gray. The evergreen trees are just starting to collect the snow, creating a scene that is far more beautiful than I feel. The cafeteria is several floors up. In the distance I can see another hospital and a skybridge that connects the two hospitals. I feel really small.

It seems fitting not to see color. Everything feels grim right now. I am past the whirlwind of activity of the morning and, for the first time, my thoughts turn to how this will all impact me. I immediately feel guilty for thinking of myself while Tim is still in the ICU, but my thoughts wander there, nonetheless.

My thoughts wander to our adoption, which is currently in process. I wonder if it will even happen now. I wonder if I will ever be a mom. I wonder if Tim will live to be a dad. I wonder if we will have to take ourselves off the wait list and give up our dream of raising a child. Over and over these thoughts circle through my mind as the snow continues to fall. I feel the chill of reality seeping in.

My thoughts are filled with questions and darkness and so much uncertainty as my husband is literally suspended in the gray space between life and death.

So Many Feelings
February 2008 – One Day After Stroke

It's Day Two.

The first day *after* Tim's stroke.

I was hoping it was all a bad dream.

It wasn't a dream.

Tim is still in the neuro-ICU and I am sleepwalking my way around the house after a very sleepless night. I am feeling pulled to write—to document what is happening—and yet I find myself strangely resistant to writing anything down for fear of making it somehow more real.

My thoughts and feelings keep shifting as I try to make sense of the unfathomable. *Back and forth. Real or not real?*

I am so exhausted. My body is an exposed nerve of brokenness and my brain can't stop rolling out scenarios. *Better or not better?* Last night the ICU nurses told me to go home and rest. They said it was important. *Stay or go?* I didn't want to leave but didn't want to make a fuss and, honestly, I wasn't even sure I had the energy to make a fuss.

My car was not at the hospital, as I had arrived in the ambulance with Tim, so I had to ask some friends to drive me home. I have no memory of the ride home. Maybe I fell asleep or maybe I just stared out the window, lost in thought. I don't know.

I sit down on the couch and curl up under a blanket, keeping my eye on the clock. I got up early and am planning to head back up to the hospital soon. I am timing my departure from home so my arrival at the hospital will happen after the shift change in the ICU, since visitors are not allowed in during that time. I prefer to sit here at home, curled up on my couch, rather than wait in another depressing hospital waiting room.

The house is strangely quiet, interrupted only by the sound of the furnace that kicks on occasionally to offset the wintry weather outside. My sweet cats jump up on the couch with me, apparently sensing my pain and wanting to comfort me. Their attunement makes me cry.

I am holding a small spiral notebook and struggling to stay grounded enough to write. I open it and start handwriting every single feeling I can remember feeling in the past twenty-four hours. I don't write full sentences or complete thoughts, as I don't have the energy to keep myself from sinking into a deep hole of grief. I tearfully write the words, feeling every single one of them as I write, bearing witness to my experience, and then simply close the notebook, set it aside, wall off that part of me, and move on with my day. *Feel or not feel?*

In this moment, I choose not to feel.

I didn't reopen that notebook again for more than a decade.
I created the following illustration from my list of words that day.

Dual Selves
February 2008 – One Day After Stroke

The light dances on the driveway as the wind blows through the large silver maple trees down by the street. It's the evening of Day Two and I am back at home, sitting at the dining room table, staring vacantly out the window at the streetlight. I cooked myself some dinner but have no appetite. I absentmindedly push the food around on my plate, watch the light outside, and wonder how long I will feel this gaping hole in my heart.

I spent the day at the hospital, watching and waiting for Tim to show signs of improvement. I wasn't even sure what I was watching for. He didn't speak. He didn't show signs of understanding anything said to him.

He wasn't *himself*, which left me feeling unlike *myself*.

I was so confused and disoriented. I reluctantly agreed to go home when the nurses encouraged me to get some rest. I didn't want to go but didn't want to stay either. I felt pretty useless. I drove home in a daze, returned a few phone calls to friends and family, made my dinner, and now sit here staring out the window, feeling just as useless at home as I felt at the hospital.

I feel myself swinging back and forth between two roles—that of a caregiver and that of a weary wife who is terrified to lose her husband. Wearing both hats at the same time feels a little too overwhelming. I prefer the caregiver role. It's definitely more familiar. As the oldest daughter and someone used to working in a helping profession, caregiving comes easy. The preference really has nothing to do with familiarity, though. I prefer it simply because it's less painful.

I get up from the table, walk to our home office, sit down at my computer, and write an optimistic email to friends and family about what happened. I do this for two reasons. One, I am so emotionally tired of reliving the story each time I tell it and, two, I know there are loved ones who will want to know what happened.

After I type the email, I send it to everyone that comes to mind and then ask a few friends to please pass it along to anyone I may have missed. It is my first act since the stroke that feels normal.

Step up, take care of things, shove the feelings aside.

Be a good caregiver.

This is the moment when I feel the shift. I realize that caregiving allows me to distance from the pain, tuck away the wounded parts, and take a little bit of control over the way I feel. I don't feel quite as useless.

I can do this.

Armed with Confusion
February 2008 – Two Days After Stroke

The constant cacophony of sound is deafening. It's Day Three in the neuro-ICU and a tray of food was just brought in. I am standing on the right side of Tim's bed, facing him. He is hooked up to machines for blood pressure, pulse, and oxygen levels, and is receiving fluids and meds through an IV in his arm. The machines beep and hum and occasionally shrill with alarm. The lighting in the room is surprisingly dim—supposedly to make the patients more comfortable, which I find absurd. There is nothing comfortable about this room or this situation.

Tim is sitting up in his hospital bed. There is a food tray on the rolling table that hovers over his lap. An occupational therapist stands on Tim's other side, encouraging him to eat by using words and hand gestures. Tim completely ignores her. I watch as he attempts to eat. He is attempting to eat something soft—something that looks like pudding. He's not swallowing well, so he can't have solid food or thin liquids.

He picks up the spoon with his dominant right hand, as if he's unaware that the right side of his body was paralyzed just a couple of days ago. He starts to lift the spoon to his mouth. It gets about a third of the way there and stops. His mouth opens, his tongue comes slightly out, and his head nods forward just a bit, but his arm doesn't move any closer to his mouth. He looks at his arm with total confusion. He tries again. And again. And again. It's excruciating to watch. Tears roll down my cheeks as I watch in utter disbelief. He eventually gives up, switches to his left hand, and is able to shakily feed himself. He seems oblivious to the therapist who is there to help him.

Tim leans back and closes his eyes, apparently exhausted from the effort of eating pudding. The therapist meets my gaze and I turn away quickly. I wipe my tears and wonder if my husband will ever be able to function on his own.

Superbowl
February 2008 – Three Days After Stroke

Day Four in the hospital.

Day Four in the neuro-ICU.

Day Four since my husband's stroke changed everything.

I speak to Tim and he seems to comprehend some of what I'm saying, but that may be wishful thinking. The doctors tell me he appears to recognize some pictures but gets confused and overwhelmed if presented with more than two options. I am told repeatedly that this will all improve. I remain hopeful *and* very skeptical. It's Day Four and he still hasn't uttered a word.

Not. One. Word.

It's almost quiet-time in the neuro-ICU and I am being asked to leave. A couple of times a day for an hour or two, all visitors are asked to leave so patients can rest and staff can do their shift change with minimal family interruptions. During that time the nurses interact with each other, pass along pertinent information, and give updates on all their current patients. TVs are turned off, lights are turned down low, and there is a small reprieve from the twenty-four-hour buzz of activity that tends to happen in ICUs.

It's also Superbowl Sunday.

Tim is a *huge* sports fan, so this morning we have the TV on to the pre-game commentary. It's just background noise. Neither one of us is paying much attention to it, but it brings me comfort to hear something other than all the beeps of the machines and the silence coming from Tim. The Giants and the Patriots are scheduled to play this afternoon and even though neither team is one of his favorites, Tim *normally* would have been watching, so the TV stays on. A nurse comes by again with a friendly reminder for me to leave soon. I let Tim know I will need to turn off the TV when I leave. He glares at me and loudly says, "Don't want to!" For a split second, I feel annoyed and start to explain, and then it hits me. He talked! He said words. Real words. Words that made sense in the context of his environment. Oh my God! He talked! I am ecstatic and I am absolutely convinced this will all soon be behind us. The nightmare will soon be over!

I am so wrong.

A few days pass and he hasn't said any more words. I learn that the first words to be spoken are often automatic or emotional expressions. He didn't have to think about what he was saying—the words were simply said in response to a feeling. I sit here in the ICU for hours, watching and waiting, wondering if I should provoke him to get him to talk. I choose not to. He's awake. He's aware. He's not communicating. He's not showing distress. He hasn't uttered another word.

I'm now a little more skeptical than hopeful.

Years later, Tim shared with me that during that time in the hospital, he believed he was in some weird dream in which everyone was speaking an alien language that made no sense. He was just hanging out, waiting for the dream to end so he could wake up and get back to his life.

The Gatekeeper
February 2008 – One Week After Stroke

When I watch my husband sleep, I can almost imagine this whole thing never happened. Almost. It's been a week since the stroke and Tim has finally moved out of the neuro-ICU. I'm sitting here in his new hospital room with a view, writing notes and watching him sleep. He is so exhausted and sleeps most of the time. I, on the other hand, can't sleep most of the time. I wonder if I will be able to sleep tonight.

I am writing an update to our friends and family in a notebook and will type it up this evening when I get home. I feel like the wife who is the gatekeeper, the cheerleader, and the case manager all bundled up into one role. I take all my roles very seriously. I let people know that the focus is now on rehabilitation. He is working with physical therapists, speech pathologists, and occupational therapists in addition to his team of stroke doctors. Now that he is out of the ICU, those specialists can spend more time with him.

I let our friends and family know we (meaning *me* in my multiple roles) are continuing to limit visitors to family and very close friends. Tim is so easily fatigued, and I want people to understand that the focus of his energy right now needs to be on healing and rehabilitation. I'm not sure if I do this for his benefit or mine. I'm not sure it really matters. I ask people to call me on my cell phone before visiting and then swear under my breath every time my phone rings. Sometimes I miss the ICU with its requirement to silence cell phones.

I am learning that very simple and routine things for me are very challenging and energy-draining for Tim. He is starting to answer yes/no questions and can respond to a few gestures, but these simple processes take a tremendous amount of effort for him. It's quite mind-boggling and illuminates just how much I take for granted. Our bodies really are a million little miracles all happening at once.

I turn my attention back to my notebook and try to figure out how to convey to his friends and family how to visit with Tim. People show up expecting to have a conversation with him and seem lost when it doesn't happen. I encourage his friends and family to talk to him, tell him stories, talk about their partners, their kids, their pets, their jobs, their travels, sports, politics, whatever. I encourage them not to ask Tim any questions. He seems to want to talk but can't, which is probably extremely frustrating for him. It seems surreal that the greatest conversationalist I know is now the one who can't talk. I ask people to imagine what questions Tim might ask them if he could talk, and encourage them to speak about those things.

I stretch and flex my hand a few times to get rid of the tension I feel from writing by hand. I feel resentful that I have to manage this nightmare. Then I feel guilty for feeling this way. I feel so very alone.

I never in my wildest dreams imagined I'd be in this position. It seems ludicrous that Tim is the one in the bed and I am his gatekeeper. I frown as I ponder the word gatekeeper. It's not quite right. I honestly feel more like a gate—*something that people pass through but don't really see.*

I wonder if this is what caregiving feels like.

I wonder if I am moving from being a person to being an object of service.

The Dismissive Card
February 2008 – One Week After Stroke

I can see buildings and trees and blue sky, which is quite different from the view from the room in the ICU that looked out to a dull concrete wall. It's early morning and I am standing in Tim's new hospital room, marveling at the view from his window to the west. Tim was moved to this room on the cardiac floor yesterday. We are both still trying to orient to the new space and to all the changes that have been happening in our lives over the past week or so.

Tim hands me a couple of cards. One is from one of his best friends and one is surprisingly from an old friend. I am confused. How did he get these? Did they visit? We are limiting visitors. People have been mailing cards to the house and I have been bringing them to him as he can't read or write or even gesture. He still can't speak or understand much at all. I am confused. I ask if any friends came to visit. My husband stares at me without answering. I know his friend had planned to visit, so I am assuming that he must have brought the cards.

I look at him. He is sitting up in bed. He looks really tired and gaunt but seems to be at peace.

I read the cards out loud to Tim. First I read the card from one friend and then the other. The sentiments are kind and thoughtful. As I set the cards aside, I feel my throat constrict and my blood feels like it is on fire. I am instantly nauseous. I am afraid I'm going to vomit, so I quickly walk to the door and out of the room. I turn left and walk to the end of the hallway and look out an enormous window that overlooks the entire city. The view is stunning. I breathe and stare and breathe and stare, wondering what the hell just happened.

I sit down on the floor beneath the window, putting my head back against the wall.

It hits me.

The cards don't include me. Even though the cards are kind and thoughtful, they are addressed only to Tim, as if this horrible, awful thing didn't also happen to me. In the messages, I don't exist, I am not impacted.

This story is not about Tim's friends. They are kind and caring people. What happened to me in that moment is something I wasn't able to clearly understand or articulate for years. My feelings were often ignored, erased, rendered invisible. As a caregiver, I became the invisible helper, the dutiful robot. As with most survivors of traumatic events, Tim was hyper-focused on what happened to him and would often loudly say to me, "This didn't happen to you!"

That wasn't true. I didn't have the stroke, but the stroke most certainly happened to me. Even though our experiences were different, I was not an unaffected bystander. My life was also flipped upside down. My dreams were also put on hold. My losses were also real.

No Room for Physical Therapy
February 2008 – Three Weeks After Stroke

I close my eyes and take a deep breath, imagining I am outside breathing clean air. It's a cold winter day and we are sitting in a small, claustrophobic office that doesn't have a window. Tim and I are meeting with a physical therapist at the rehabilitation center in Portland. Speech therapy, occupational therapy, and physical therapy services are all held in this big, beautiful space with tiny little meeting rooms along an inside wall. We've been here a couple of times for speech therapy and today we are here for Tim's physical therapy assessment. He had PT services in the hospital, but this is his first visit in an outpatient setting. He has been doing fairly well with walking but tends to drag his right foot. Additionally his right hand and arm don't work as he expects them to. I am hopeful they can help him with these issues.

I am sitting in with him for the talking portion of the assessment, answering all the questions I can for the therapist. Tim is not able to answer any questions on his own. I'm not even sure he understands the questions. The therapist seems annoyed with him and talks way too fast, which irritates me. After far too many questions, we all leave the office and move to a large open space just down the hall. I stand on the edge of the room as the physical therapist and Tim walk over to a space next to a wall where she instructs him to stop and then she asks him to walk toward her. She gestures to him as if to a dog and he walks toward her, looking confused. She then asks him to turn around to the left. He looks at her blankly. He looks to me for help and I don't know what to do. I just stand there. She asks him again to turn around to the left. He clearly has no idea what she is saying. She abruptly walks over to me and asks that he not return to be assessed again until he has done more speech therapy and has some ability to understand speech.

I stand there speechless as she walks away. I wonder what the hell just happened. Tim had physical therapy in the hospital. Why can't they help him here? I am in over my head. I have no idea how to advocate for him or if he even needs this service. His doctor referred him, so I assume he does. It's all so overwhelming and confusing. I don't know what to do or say, so we just put on our coats and head for the elevator. As the elevator travels to the dark parking garage, I silently curse this fucked-up situation.

Looking back, I wonder why that therapist didn't work with Tim. I know there are other clients out there with aphasia who also need help with their physical mobility challenges. That was just one of many times when Tim's needs were ignored because he couldn't clearly articulate them. I was simply the wife. I didn't yet have the skills to be his medical case manager, his medical advocate.

Indefinite Leave of Absence
February 2008 – Three Weeks After Stroke

I stare at the piles of documents in front of me and feel completely overwhelmed. Even though the papers covering our large dining room table are neatly stacked and organized, it still feels chaotic. To cope with the anxiety this messiness is causing, I've been making lists in an attempt to sort and prioritize all the things I need to do. There are documents and requests from the health insurance company, from Tim's employer, from my employer, from all the doctors involved, and from family and friends who all want to be kept in the loop. I see the paperwork for Tim's medical leave from work and the paperwork I am filling out for him to get short-term disability benefits. I have to contact his doctors to get them to fill out lots of forms *in a timely manner* which have to be mailed or faxed or overnighted, depending on the recipient. It's completely crazy-making. I put my head in my hands and take a few deep breaths, feeling very alone and incompetent.

I look at a document signed by one of Tim's neurologists. The doctor indicates, in writing, that Tim could *possibly* make a full recovery in about a year. It's not a promise but it does provide some hope and I find myself smiling.

When I submitted documents to the human resources department of Tim's employer a couple of days ago, they granted him an "indefinite leave of absence" from his job. I was stunned. I had never heard of this. On the other hand, my employer of more than ten years granted me three months of family leave, with lots of reminders that I would be terminated if it continued beyond that. The difference between the two responses is pretty disheartening.

I shake away the memory of my employer's stance and try to focus on the tasks at hand—the things I need to do. I send off a few emails and fill out yet another form. I do a little research on Social Security disability benefits, which I have been told Tim may need if he is going to be off work for a year or so. I wonder if this kind of case-management activity will be my new full-time job. I wonder if my husband will recover and go back to work. I wonder if he will be well enough in three months for me to return to my job so I can avoid termination.

As I think about his indefinite leave of absence, I am struck by just how great Tim must be at his job. I am also struck by how much he loves his work. I wonder how often those things align. Tim knew what he wanted to do when he was thirteen years old and it has always been a source of joy for him.

I feel my blood run cold at the thought that he may not recover enough to go back to work. *What if he can't go back? What if he can't type or talk or create? What if he can no longer do that thing he loves most?* The blood clot that caused his stroke was lodged right in the language center of his brain. A couple of Tim's many gifts are computer languages and being able to communicate with others about those languages. Some of his other gifts include being social, being curious, being a talker. *What if?*

Sometimes the unfairness of life overwhelms me, and then it punches me right in the throat.

Stop Hitting Me
February 2008 – Four Weeks After Stroke

I cringe as I feel Tim hit my upper arm. It's his way of getting my attention and it drives me bat shit crazy. Over and over, I have asked him not to hit me, but he continues. It's been a month or so since the stroke and he still doesn't use words to ask for what he wants—maybe he can't find them, or maybe he's simply afraid of saying something wrong. We are in an elevator and I breathe a sigh of relief that no one is here to witness his behavior.

We exit the elevator in the medical building and turn right, heading for another bank of elevators to take us to the rehabilitation center where Tim has speech therapy several times per week. After coming from the dimly lit underground parking garage, stepping into a large, cavernous lobby with lots of natural light feels almost painful. I close my eyes and squint until it's more comfortable. Windows rise up two floors and bathe the lobby in morning sun from the eastern sky. It's absolutely glorious.

I hate the hitting. I'm sure Tim thinks he's lightly tapping me, but since his stroke and the temporary paralysis, he doesn't have a good sense of his own strength. Sometimes he lightly touches me and sometimes he delivers a blow that results in bruising. I go into fight-or-flight mode every damned time and have to take deep breaths, slow my heart rate, and try to respond without screaming at him. I don't want my husband to hit me to get my attention and I honestly don't know how to stop it.

As we step into the area outside the elevators that go to the rehabilitation floor, I turn and yell at him to *stop hitting me*. People turn to stare. I don't even care. I just want it to stop. We step into the elevator, standing a few feet apart as I hit the button to the fourth floor.

It took months for Tim to stop that behavior. Even though it simultaneously broke my heart and threw me into fight mode almost every time, I learned to tolerate his almost instinctual drive to get my attention. Most of us are blessed to be able to use language for this. Without that option, gestures became his habit of choice. I have a deep sense of compassion for those who are ill and described as "combative." I wonder if they are just wanting to speak and can't. I also wonder if their caregivers are also wanting to speak and can't.

Making Lemonade
February 2008 – Four Weeks After Stroke

The house is all decked out with balloons, flowers, and colorful table-cloths. It's surprisingly festive and I feel myself smiling. It's Saturday afternoon, about a month after Tim's stroke, and we are having a party. Call me crazy. This is what we would *normally* be doing, so it's what I planned. I keep thinking that if we go on about our normal life, maybe things will swing back into their rightful places. So far, it hasn't worked, but I'm not ready to throw in the towel yet. Maybe this party will help.

Tim, the extrovert in our marriage, loves parties. He loves talking and socializing and laughing and being around lots and lots of people. I, on the other hand, as an introvert, prefer these things in much smaller doses. I decide that having an open house for people to stop by and visit for a brief time is preferable to having to coordinate many visits.

Tim was not excited about this party. He couldn't articulate why, so I just kept reassuring him it would be fabulous. Now the day is here and the house is packed with people and food and flowers and cards and all the energy that comes with large groups of people who genuinely care about each other. Tim is smiling for the first time in a month. That smile is worth all the preparation and exhaustion and socializing. God, I've missed his smile.

As the saying goes, when life gives you lemons, make lemonade. I make a whole lot of lemonade today. Maybe there really will be a sweet ending to this challenging time.

OPEN HOUSE

So, the saying goes,
"When life gives you lemons, make lemonade."

Tim and Devon got some extra lemons recently, so
they're having a little gathering and serving up some
lemonade (and cake and cookies too).

Come on by and say hi to Tim and Devon
and see for yourself how well Tim's recovering.

Very Casual
Kids Welcome

If you can't make it but want to visit sometime,
just give us a call.

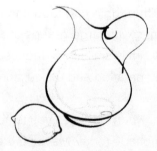

Waiting in Line
March 2008 – Six Weeks After Stroke

The line in front of us seems to go on for miles. Tim and I are heading to the Grenadines for a week of sailing and then on to Barbados for a relaxing week on land. We're hoping to get some much-needed rest and relaxation and we are currently stuck in an airport in Chicago. It's only been about six weeks since Tim's stroke and although he is alert and seems up for the adventure, he still can't speak much. This trip has been planned for months and we are relieved that Tim's physical health has improved enough for us to get approval from his doctors to go on this vacation. The neurologist requested we take multiple flights, to allow for walking between flights, and also encouraged walking periodically while on the flights. Even though scuba diving and driving were not approved for Tim, I am trying to keep my eyes on the prize: sunshine, snorkeling, and sailing after a cold and dreary winter that has brought rain, rain, and more rain.

We've already been traveling for hours. We've completed the first leg of our journey and still have three more flights to go. I am hopeful we will make all of our connections so we can catch our scheduled ferry to the island of Bequia. We have a sailboat and some dear friends waiting for us there.

Our flight from Chicago to San Juan was cancelled about thirty minutes ago due to mechanical problems. After getting back off the plane that we had already boarded, we are now waiting in a really long line to get rebooked. We are tired and the people around us are cranky and complaining. Tim is oblivious to it all and I am relieved we don't have to fly on a broken plane. I wonder why these passengers aren't grateful the problem was caught before we got in the air.

The line is barely moving. I am bored and getting tired of my own thoughts. Travelers all around us are irritable and it's starting to mess with my vacation vibe. I'm getting anxious and can feel the tension in my body. I can feel my own anxiety as well as the anxiety of others around me that I seem to be absorbing. Tim taps my arm and I feel myself flinch. He tries to say something. I wonder what he's trying to say. He's looking around. I wonder if he needs to go to the restroom. That must be it. He looks around again. I scan the room. I have no idea where the closest restroom is and don't see any signs. Damn it. A new wave of anxiety floods through me as I try to figure out how to stay in line and go find a restroom at the same time. *I want the old Tim. I want the man who was able to do this for himself.*

I take a few deep breaths. I ask the people closest to me in line if they know where the restrooms are located. No one seems to know. *Shit.* I tell Tim to stay, feeling bad that I sound like I am talking to a dog. Tim stays in line as I run to a nearby newsstand and ask for restroom directions then return to give the directions to Tim. He has no idea what I am saying. Of course he doesn't; he has aphasia. How could I forget that? I reluctantly ask the grumpy woman behind me to please hold our spot in line. I quickly walk Tim to the restroom and then wait outside the door so he can find his way back. We return to find the line hasn't moved at all.

The minutes slowly tick by and Tim is visibly exhausted. He takes a seat in a nearby chair and falls asleep as I continue to stand in line, keeping an eye on him while waiting for our turn. I look at him and feel a huge wave of apprehension. I am starting to see how truly dependent he is on me.

Lost on a Train
March 2008 – Six Weeks After Stroke

grab a pole and hold on as the train picks up speed. Tim and I are on a crowded train in a large airport moving from one terminal to another, continuing on our way to the Caribbean for our much-needed sailing vacation. I am still amazed that I managed to convince Tim's doctors to give us the green light to go on this trip.

Tim's global aphasia is still severe—he can only speak a few words. His understanding of language is minimal at best. I know he wants to go on this trip as much as I do—anything to step back into what is normal for us. I spend a ton of time making sure the trip will work for him—alerting the sailing crew to our circumstances, getting instructions from his doctors for the air travel and seasickness if needed, and making sure he has all the gear he needs.

The train is packed with people. We are both standing up, holding on to vertical metal poles, trying to keep from falling as the train accelerates and decelerates rather quickly. I am caught up in the excitement that always hits me when going on a trip. I am chatting away to Tim about the weather, the terminal where we will get off, how much time we have until our next flight, yada, yada, yada, completely forgetting that Tim has no idea what I am saying. The train stops and I quickly exit the train, wheeling my carry-on bag behind me. I stop and turn around just as the doors are starting to close. I look up and feel the rush of panic. *Where is Tim?* I run to the train, throwing my body in front of the door so it won't close. I yell at Tim to get off the train. The adrenalin is coursing through my blood. I am single-focused, wild-eyed, and probably a little scary.

Tim is completely oblivious. I realize in this precise moment that I failed to really think about what I might need on this trip in my role as his newly acquired caregiver. We haven't even left the country and I'm starting to wonder if I've overestimated how relaxing this trip might be.

Turtle-Watching
March 2008 – Seven Weeks After Stroke

The turquoise blue water beckons to us as we sit on the back of the sailboat. Tim and I are putting on our snorkeling gear, excited to get in the water and see some turtles. It still seems surreal to be here after Tim's recent stroke. It's a beautiful sunny day and we are blessed to be in the Southern Grenadines in the Caribbean. It's a place we both love; a place I like to call Heaven.

We are at the Baradel Turtle Sanctuary in the Tobago Cays Marine Park. It's a protected area where we can snorkel around and see both green and hawksbill turtles in their natural environment. I am so excited to be here and can't wait to get in the water. Tim, a scuba diver for many years, loves the sun and the water and seems happy to be here as well. This is our first sailing trip since the stroke, so both of us are feeling a little apprehensive. We've been on this trip before, and I'm hoping that doing something familiar will be restorative for both of us after the rollercoaster of the past couple of months.

We put on our fins and masks and climb down the ladder from the boat, testing out our snorkel masks before swimming off in the direction of the turtle sanctuary. I am anxious and keeping a pretty close eye on Tim. The water's not too deep and he appears to be swimming comfortably. I feel myself relax a little.

The turtles are everywhere. They are diving down and feeding and then coming up to the surface for air. They seem oblivious to the humans swimming in their space. It's truly amazing. I pop up out of the water and ask Tim if he sees the turtles. He shakes his head. We put our faces back in the water and I point to some turtles right in front of us. Tim seems confused. I wonder if his vision is impaired. I wonder if he's not okay. I motion for us to head back to the boat. We've only been in the water for about ten minutes and Tim looks very cold and uncomfortable.

We swim to the boat and as he gets out of the water, I see that he is visibly shaking from the cold—full body shaking. I am alarmed. He lost some weight in the hospital and is definitely a little underweight. I wonder if that's why he's so cold. I help him wrap up in a couple of towels and move to a place on the deck in the sun where he can warm up. I am usually the one who gets cold on these trips, so I am very confused by his response.

His shaking subsides as he warms up and I ask him again about the turtles. He shakes his head when I ask if he saw them. I finally get out the fish book and show him a photo. He lights up. He saw those. He looks at the photo and says "turtle" as if it's a new word he just heard for the first time. It breaks my heart.

After returning home a couple of weeks later and following up with his stroke doctors, we learned that Tim's brain is not able to quickly regulate his body temperature on the right side of his body—the side where he was paralyzed for a time following the stroke. His body responds to cold and heat but much more slowly than before. He has had to learn to use his left hand (his non-dominant hand) to test shower and tap water so he won't inadvertently scald himself. When swimming, he now wears a wetsuit and limits his time in the water to keep from getting uncomfortably cold.

Navigating New Roads
March 2008 – Two Months After Stroke

I turn the car to the left into another roundabout and Tim holds up three fingers. I count the streets and exit to the left on the third one. I breathe a sigh of relief and wonder if we are on the right road. Still on vacation, now on the island of Barbados, we have finally found our rhythm—with Tim as the navigator and me as the driver. Driving on the left side of the road in a car with the steering wheel on the right has been an interesting and somewhat frightening experience. It's like learning to drive all over again but without the overconfidence of my teenage self.

We have spent time on this island before, so it is somewhat familiar, which is helpful. We are staying on a part of the island that is fairly quiet and doesn't have a ton of traffic, which makes driving a little less challenging. We are using a paper map to navigate the island and it has been quite the comedy show. Tim is not able to read at all, speaks very little, and understands even less, yet he seems to be able to count on his fingers and read a map. *Brain injuries are weird*. He tells me where to turn by holding up fingers to tell me how many roads to pass before I turn. He gets left and right mixed up, so I pull over after each turn and get my bearings.

We've been through this roundabout several times now, but we are managing to find our way around the island and I think we may be on the right road. I pull the little blue rental car over onto the left shoulder of the road and check the map, pointing to the next turn as we head toward our destination. He nods and I cautiously pull back out onto the road and we continue on our way.

We are heading to a little pottery shop we discovered here on a previous trip. It will be nice to visit someplace that is familiar and meaningful. So much of this trip over the past couple of weeks has been about learning to navigate life in a very new way. After our week on a sailboat, we are now spending a week on land. We are both exhausted and I just want to experience something that can be done with ease.

As I drive, I think about Tim's brain injury and how he is now forced to process information in a completely new way, laying down a bunch of new neural pathways all at once. It's similar in some ways to what I am experiencing driving a car on the left side of the road from the right side of the car. Driving feels familiar but totally different all at the same time. I turn and smile at Tim, feeling a huge wave of compassion for him as he is forced to lay down new neural pathways and learn to navigate new roads in every freaking area of his life.

Go Fish
March 2008 – Two Months After Stroke

All of the windows are open, letting in warm sunshine and a lovely ocean breeze. Tim and I are seated facing each other on opposite ends of a large white sofa. I slip off my sandals and tuck my bare feet under me. It feels so good to be wearing shorts and a t-shirt after a cold and wet winter back home in Oregon. We are staying at a beautiful resort on the island of Barbados. I can see the ocean from our room and hear the crashing of the waves on the beach down below. It is absolutely heavenly.

We are playing another round of Go Fish, a card game we both learned as kids but haven't played in years. Conversations are a challenge as Tim is not able to speak very many words or understand much of what he hears. We've been traveling for about a week and a half, and though we've been on many adventures on this trip, we are mostly on our own with each other and, quite frankly, I have run out of monologues. I crave conversation.

A couple of days ago I saw a deck of cards in the hotel gift shop and purchased them on impulse. I thought maybe we could play some games to pass the time. We tried Crazy Eights and Gin Rummy, but they were a little too confusing, so we landed on Go Fish.

I ask Tim if he has any fives, and he gives me a completely blank look. I then hold up five fingers. He shakes his head, signaling for me to draw a card. I draw a card and look at him. He holds up two fingers and I search my hand for a two and shake my head as well, signaling for him to draw a card. And so it goes, game after game after game. It's a rather quiet game, but it serves to pass the time between other activities and probably has the added benefit of connecting some neural pathways in Tim's brain.

We both seem to enjoy the reprieve from what has become our lives. Tim seemed reluctant to play this game at first—maybe hesitant to play something simple that is typically reserved for children—but I can see now that he is happy to be communicating and engaging in something that doesn't leave him totally perplexed. I look up from my cards and stare out the window at the blue sky and the deep blue of the Atlantic Ocean. I am filled with awe. In moments like these I can almost imagine that this too shall pass; that all will be well. I *almost* let myself wonder if someday we will come back here and play this game with our children.

Web of Care
March 2008 – Two Months After Stroke

I slam down the phone and burst into tears. Although it's been a couple of months since Tim's stroke, I am still trying to wrap my head around the web of care necessary for his recovery. Managing his disability insurance, his medical leave from work, his health insurance benefits, his speech therapy, his appointments with the neurologist, and his appointments with his primary care physician is a full-time job. How can I be the only one who is navigating and managing this? Why are all of Tim's providers not talking to each other?

I am still shaking as I think about the call that just ended. I was speaking with a customer service representative from Tim's health insurance provider. We received a statement in the mail saying the claim for anesthesia was denied because anesthesia is considered an "alternative treatment." *What the bloody hell? Have we gone back to the Dark Ages? Did they expect Tim to bite on a leather strap while a neurosurgeon extracted a blood clot from his brain?* The representative blandly assured me, "It was an error" and "of course the anesthesia would be covered," once I called the hospital and asked them to resubmit the claim.

If this were an isolated incident, I would probably laugh about the absurdity of it and move on. But it's not. Earlier this week I had a conversation with this same insurance provider about a single day in the middle of Tim's hospital stay that they were claiming was not covered by his insurance. He had insurance benefits the day before and the day after but *not on that one random day*. It made no sense. (It still doesn't.) That representative blandly assured me, "It was an error" and "of course, all of the hospital stay would be covered." I am starting to wonder if all claims run through a random claim-denial process, bumping out claims randomly for random reasons, with the hope that some random people will overlook them and just make the payment anyway. I wonder what people do if they are unmarried, unpartnered, or don't have friends or family members who are able to step up and take care of this part of the process. I think I am starting to become very jaded about insurance companies.

I take a few deep breaths, blow my nose, check this insurance call off my to-do list, and then, with much irritation, add a call to the hospital regarding this claim to the bottom of the same very long list.

I move down the list and make another call—this one to a physiatrist, a rehabilitation specialist who works in the area. A friend had recommended I consider having Tim work with this specialist so his rehabilitation care needs could be managed and coordinated by someone other than me. I talk for a while with an assistant, and it all sounds fabulous until they let me know that unfortunately, Tim's insurance doesn't cover this service. I choke back tears, thank her for her time and hang up the phone sobbing.

I wonder how I can return to full-time work. I'm not even sure I can return to part-time work. I wonder how I will be able to manage the paperwork necessary to keep him in good standing with his job. The requirements for short-term disability benefits, long-term disability benefits, and disability insurance claims are quite daunting—all requiring paperwork to be completed by the employee (or representative) as well as by the medical providers. How will I be able to manage to get him to speech therapy appointments three times a week and the doctor appointments that always fall during business hours, which are also *my* working hours? I feel the pressure of my own family leave coming to an end in a month unless I am able to spread it out with intermittent leave. The pressure from all directions feels completely overwhelming.

I take a deep breath and cross the physiatrist off my list and close my notebook. I can't make another call today. I know I need to rest. I know I am dealing with a system that is broken. The supportive web of healthcare in this country is an illusion that disappears the second you really need it.

Lost Memories
March 2008 – Two Months After Stroke

Nothing feels ordinary right now and I'm surprised how much I miss that feeling. It's been a couple of intense months since Tim's stroke and we are more determined than ever to get back to engaging in ordinary life events. Today it feels good to be out and about running errands. It's an early spring morning on a weekday and Tim and I are currently at our neighborhood grocery store picking up a few items. I am grateful to see the store is busy but not overly crowded, leaving me feeling a little hopeful that this trip to the store might feel sort of normal.

Prior to the stroke, Tim and I established a routine of doing our grocery shopping together because, frankly, we both hate grocery shopping and doing it together meant we could get it over with much more quickly. It worked for us. This is the first time he's been in a grocery store since the stroke and it's going fairly well. He appears content to be pushing the cart while I grab things off the shelves. It feels nice to be doing something familiar.

We finish our hunting and gathering and get in line to check out. Tim pulls out his wallet and says he will pay. I look at him quizzically. We've already been down this road. He doesn't remember any of his passwords or the PIN number for his debit card. I ask him if he remembers his code and he stares at me blankly. Again, he says he will use his card. I acknowledge what he said and ask if he remembers the code. The blank stare continues. He has no idea what I'm talking about. He says he will use his card in the machine. I nod and ask if he knows the code for his card. He's getting irritated now. I back off, feeling my own irritation starting to rise.

The checker scans and bags our groceries. Tim inserts his card in the machine and looks perplexed when the display requires a code. He looks at me and raises his eyebrows. I shrug. I don't know his code. We have been married for more than a decade and have never shared our passwords or PIN numbers. We are in our forties—both in great health (except for the unexplained large stroke he just had) and it didn't even occur to us to take these steps. He continues to stare at the machine, ignoring the checker who is now trying to help him through it. He doesn't try any codes. He doesn't even understand what it means to have a code. I pull his card out of the machine, hand it back to him, insert my own card, and complete the transaction. He continues to look at me like I'm an alien who has just done something incredibly bizarre. I can feel the heat in my face. I quickly apologize to the checker and to the line behind us and we leave the store in a cloud of frustration.

I sit in the driver's seat of our car wondering how the hell I am going to keep going. I am burning with embarrassment and dread. I wonder why we didn't share our passwords. I wonder why we didn't plan for disasters. Will things ever go back to normal, or are we destined to stay in this space of lost memories and confusion and long silences? I wonder for the millionth time *what else don't I know that I should know?*

After the Stroke

His body, near fatally broken
heals and lives
It's a miracle!
What a blessing!
Everyone breathes
a collective sigh
of relief

Except his wife
who lost her husband
She is slowly
breaking apart
drowning in pain
as the crowd
continues to cheer

Kissing a Stranger
March 2008 – Two Months After Stroke

It's early afternoon on a lovely spring day. Tim and I are on the small sidewalk between our driveway and the front porch, walking up to the house. Tim draws me into a hug, leans down, and kisses me on the mouth. I feel myself cringe and pull away. My response is weird. I don't know how to make sense of it. The kiss felt wrong. It's as if some random stranger just walked up here and kissed me. This stranger looks like my husband, but my body doesn't believe my eyes. I am so confused. I am both embarrassed by my reaction of pulling away and oddly justified by it as well. It doesn't feel right to kiss a stranger. God, this is messed up. I turn and quickly run to the front door, leaving my husband standing there wondering what the hell just happened.

I go to my office, wake up my computer, and pull up my journal, wondering if writing my thoughts will help me make sense of them. It doesn't help. I know him. I know his kiss. We've been together for fourteen years. *Did the stroke have to take everything?* I don't recall reading anything in the information about strokes indicating my husband might one day feel like a stranger.

There are so many losses that have been in our faces from day one—aphasia, paralysis, loss of oxygen to parts of the brain, balance issues, challenges with swallowing, inability to communicate, lack of independence, emotional challenges, increased fear and anxiety—to name a few. These were all talked about and expected. What I didn't expect were all the hidden losses that are slowly being revealed. What I didn't expect was to have my husband's kisses no longer feel familiar to me.

A couple of the ways I learned to make sense of that experience was to liken it to being in an arranged marriage or being with someone's twin. That didn't make the situation any better, but it helped my brain to stop being so confused. In many ways today, I still feel as if the man I married is gone and was replaced by his twin. He looks like Tim but, in many ways, he is so very different.

Really Smart Friends
April 2008 – Three Months After Stroke

Following Tim's release from the hospital a few months ago, a friend of mine set up a meal train—not only to help us out by providing meals but also to make sure that *both* of us will have visitors during this hellish time. The meals are a gift. The visits are a balm on all the sadness that sits in our house. Sometimes people drop off food, sometimes they stay and share a meal. I am touched each and every time someone knocks on the door.

Today our lunch was brought by some of Tim's closest friends. The four men (including Tim), who are all in their forties or fifties, met more than a decade ago while working together in the high-tech world. They are fun and interesting and make the effort to get together often. I opt not to eat with them—giving Tim space to be with his friends on his own. The smell of amazing Thai food fills the air, leaving me hungering for both food and connection. It's strange to hear so much talking and laughing happening in our home. I didn't realize how much I missed hearing laughter and friendly banter.

I eat while standing at the small island in our kitchen, staring at a book while half-listening as the guys visit in the dining room a few steps away. I hear them talking about history and politics and computers and art and travel and cooking and sports. I am a little baffled. They all seem really smart. How did I not know this?

I know that Tim is really smart. It wasn't the first thing I was drawn to back when we met, but I knew the intelligence was there. I knew he worked as an engineer and I knew he loved his work, even if he didn't necessarily like the company he was working for at the time. Mostly,

I liked that he was kind and that we had great conversations about anything and everything. I liked that he was a great communicator and a great listener. I liked that we worked in different fields and brought different gifts to our relationship.

Even though I find myself feeling a tad bit inferior right now, I am grateful Tim's intellect has never been thrown in my face. I realize Tim and I have strengths in different areas, and I know we complement each other well, but I am still a little surprised by his friends. In this moment, I can feel the magnitude of another loss he is experiencing. What if he doesn't recover? To lose the capacity for language while retaining your intelligence is bad enough. To lose your ability to communicate with your friends is something straight out of hell.

I return my attention to the guys in the dining room who are now discussing something related to gravity or physics or some such thing, and I wonder if Tim will ever return to the work he loves. With a deep sense of foreboding, I wonder if his really smart friends will stick around if he doesn't.

Dragon Speak
April 2008 – Three Months After Stroke

This is not our typical trip to a bookstore. Tim and I are on a mission. We are standing in a spacious Barnes & Noble in the local mall, staring at the books available on CD. I am looking for *The Pillars of the Earth* by Ken Follett, the book that Tim was reading prior to his stroke. I am a little shocked by both the high prices and how one book requires so many audio CDs. I pick up the box and scan the other titles that are available. It's mostly bestsellers. I shake my head, still somewhat mystified by this different way of reading.

Tim wants to get back to speaking, reading, and writing. He wants it *right now*. I am determined to do whatever I can to help him find his way back to communicating, but I am feeling pretty overwhelmed and a little frustrated by the lack of support available. I'm not giving up yet.

Sadly, the medical world appears to be light-years behind the world of technology. Speech therapy is amazing, but even with three appointments a week, it's not enough. There are so many other hours in a week that are without speech support. I've been going to all of Tim's speech therapy appointments with him so I can learn how to best assist with his homework, but learning to speak as an adult after a brain injury (a brain injury in the language center, no less) is far more complicated than learning through immersion as a child. Tim's apraxia results in his mouth not knowing or remembering how to form sounds. His expressive aphasia makes it difficult to find the sounds or words he wants to express, and his receptive aphasia makes it challenging for him to fully understand spoken language. It's pretty daunting and I am clearly in way over my head. Again.

I have been researching rehabilitation suggestions and discovered there are some promising technologies that are starting to hit the market. Medical transcription has been around for a while and those technologies are now slowly becoming available to the public to support those with disabilities. I had hoped Tim's speech therapist could offer some ideas for what additional tools might be helpful for regaining speech more quickly and effectively. Even though she's heard of a few things out there, she wasn't able to specifically recommend anything. I realize yet again that we (meaning mostly me) are on our own.

We are driving home after purchasing the audio CDs and Tim says something and then immediately follows it up with the question, "What did I say?" One of the quirky things he often does is ask me to write down what he has just said. He carries a small notebook and pen with him and when he says something, he hands me the notebook and says, "What did I say?" He hears his words, but even his own words sound foreign to him and often he has no idea what he just said. I roll my eyes and dutifully pull over and park so I can write his words in his notebook. Although his notebook feedback system is clever and very useful to him, it has become incredibly burdensome and annoying to me. This routine happens many times a day and often stops the flow of any conversation. I know there must be a better way for him to get this feedback.

Until the stroke, Tim was always the tech-savvy person in our marriage. I can find my way around Word, Excel, and Publisher. I'm getting more comfortable with Internet searches but find I am easily sidetracked and wind up going down a bunch of rabbit holes. Tim wants to use technology as a tool. Because I recently read that people who have aphasia do better when communication is presented to them in more than one way, such as hearing *and* seeing a word at the same time, we are exploring books on CDs, which he can listen to while following along in the book.

We arrive home with the audio CDs that go with the print book version he was reading before the stroke and, in doing so, we take this small but mighty step toward using technology in his recovery, hoping it will reap measurable rewards on the road to communication; hoping technology can become a pillar of his recovery.

That box of audio CDs was the first technological tool in the recovery toolbox. After the CDs were a big hit, we went on to purchase the Dragon Naturally Speaking software, which allowed Tim to say words out loud and then instantly see them on a computer screen. (Voice memos on phones debuted a year later.) He used the Dragon software at first for one or two words at a time and then moved up to sending emails.

We also purchased a tool called Natural Reader, which basically could read out loud any selected text on a computer screen, such as emails, web pages, and eventually computer code. By getting the information into his brain in multiple ways, Tim was much more likely to quickly and effectively understand both what he himself was saying and what he was hearing or reading. The use of those tools catapulted his recovery and his independence, and ultimately shifted him away from relying on me for everything.

Who Are You?
April 2008 – Three Months After Stroke

It's been a few months since Tim's stroke, and we are slowly falling into a new way of being with each other. I am exhausted and overwhelmed and hypersensitive to everything. In contrast, Tim is somewhat disconnected and oblivious to the hardships of daily life. He doesn't seem anxious. He doesn't seem depressed. As a psychotherapist, I am continually on the lookout for signs of either—adding to my own hypersensitivity and discomfort. It's disconcerting to me that he isn't more anxious and depressed. It doesn't make logical sense.

It's a random weekday and we are currently at home, where we spend most of our time when not at medical appointments. I am busy preparing dinner. Tim is in the living room, sitting peacefully in a large brown chair under the front window. It's quiet in the house. The TV is distressing to him so it's not on. I walk from the kitchen to the living room and let him know dinner is almost ready. He looks right at me and loudly says, *"Fuck you."*

I am shocked. Stunned.

I stand here as if he has just slapped me across the face. I can't wrap my head around it. Tim doesn't swear. Ever. I am the one who swears. Tim has never been verbally violent with me. Not once in the fourteen years we've been together. I have never even heard him use the f-word. I open my mouth to respond, and no words come out. I just stand here staring at him. I finally find my voice and whisper, *"Who are you?"* Then I burst into tears and run from the room.

On that day, I had no idea that swearing when frustrated is common for those with aphasia, even for those who didn't swear before.

Years later, Tim and I talked about that painful interaction. The memory is burned in my brain, but he has no recollection of it at all.

Two of the most distressing things I experienced following his brain injury were 1) the personality changes that made him act in ways that were so out of character and 2) the tremendous unraveling of our connection that happened as a result.

Social Security Dilemma
April 2008 – Three Months After Stroke

After we pass through a metal detector and I have my purse searched by an armed guard, we sign in at a kiosk and sit down to wait for our appointment. It's a weekday morning and Tim and I are at our very "welcoming" local Social Security office.

After about thirty minutes of waiting, we are directed through a locked door and into a carpeted hallway. The hallway is lined with windows that look out to a parking lot on one side and windows into a large bullpen office area on the other. The walls are painted a depressing shade of beige and there is nothing warm or inviting about the space. We take a seat at one of the service windows, as instructed. The window into the office is constructed of bulletproof glass with a few holes in it for voices to carry through. There is a space at the bottom of the glass to slide documents back and forth. There are no dividers between us and the other people here today, so no sense of privacy whatsoever. We are all sitting at one long continuous counter in this hallway. We are all yelling in order to be heard through the holes. The woman who is helping Tim and me seems bored and irritated. It's clear she doesn't want to be here anymore than we do.

It's been a few months since Tim's stroke. We are here because we have been told that Tim's long-term disability benefits (provided through an insurance company) will not be paid to him unless he also applies for Social Security. If he receives Social Security benefits, those amounts will be deducted from his insurance payments.

I am struggling with the wording on the application. The Social Security application requires Tim (or his caregiver) to make a case for "permanent" disability, even though he is still hoping for a full recovery and a return to work as soon as possible. How does someone ethically do this? It feels like a lie. It feels like duress. The insurance company is asking us to make a valid case for permanent disability and are threatening to cut off Tim's benefits if it's not done. The truth is, we don't know if he'll recover, but the Social Security application is so black and white. There is no middle option. There is no option for explaining what is happening. I have so many questions and I feel my blood boiling as my questions keep getting dismissed and ignored.

So here we sit, in this fucking hallway full of sadness, devoid of hope, with me trying to explain this stupid dilemma to a person who seems to have lost her connection to humanity. I can feel my anger rising. My palms are sweating as I try repeatedly to rephrase my questions. The caseworker is unimpressed and rolls her eyes. She keeps trying to speak to Tim. He has no idea what she is saying, and I keep trying to explain that to her. She clearly doesn't know what aphasia is and continues to ignore me as I seethe with frustration.

I am starting to see why there is protective glass in the Social Security Office.

The Alphabet Song
April 2008 – Three Months After Stroke

It's a lovely spring morning and traffic is light as we make our way across the river and into the heart of the city. It's been three months since Tim's stroke and I am driving him to a speech therapy appointment. We make this trek several times a week and I wonder how other stroke survivors do this if they are unpartnered or if their partner has to work. I'm pretty sure all the speech therapy appointments are scheduled during the day. The thought leaves me feeling disturbingly sad.

Tim is making some progress in his ability to speak. Because of his apraxia, his mouth does not "remember" how to form sounds, and some information is currently not moving from his brain to his mouth. I'm not sure if it's memory loss or signals not getting through. Consequently, he is learning to speak all over again, one painstaking sound at a time. It's excruciating to watch. *Hold your tongue this way. Hold your lips in this position. Touch the roof of your mouth with your tongue. Close your teeth and blow out. Etc. Etc. Etc.* I am so astonished by how freaking complicated it is to make even the simplest meaningful sound with our mouths.

Tim is learning to say the ABCs. He is able to sing the children's alphabet song but can't yet speak it. Evidently, music lives in a different part of the brain—not in the language center where Tim sustained the most damage during his stroke. He can sing the song but can't actually understand what he's singing, and speaking each letter on its own is still a huge challenge. Because Tim has always been super motivated, practicing speech exercises is something he willingly and diligently does, day after day after day. He completes every single assignment given to him.

As we drive along, he is practicing the alphabet. "A B C D K K K K K L L L L M M M M M M M..." I look over at him and ask him to stop. He looks at me with confusion. He repeats the letters again. "A B C D K K K K K L L L L M M M M M M M..." I ask him again to stop, this time with more irritation in my voice. I try to explain that what he is saying is not the alphabet; what he is doing is laying down memory that is just plain *wrong*. I'm not kind. He ignores me. He truly believes he is saying the alphabet just as he knows it and hears it in his mind. I am so frustrated I could scream. I threaten to tell his speech therapist what he's doing and feel strangely comforted by this, as if I truly have an ally in this hellish little nightmare we're in. He shuts up and we ride the rest of the way in uncomfortable silence.

We arrive at the rehabilitation center in a cloud of frustration. He's frustrated with me. I'm frustrated with him. We're both frustrated with all things related to this stupid stroke. I tell on him. I feel a rush of relief as I tell the story to his speech therapist and then immediately am flooded with nausea. I hope I don't throw up. His therapist asks him not to practice the alphabet anymore until he has had more sessions. He readily agrees, throwing me a look that says he would rather listen to her than listen to me. I glare at him. Then I get up, excuse myself from their session, and go to the nearest restroom and cry without opening my mouth or making a single sound.

I Have No Voice
May 2008 – Four Months After Stroke

The large, sunlit training room at my office is filled with about twenty-five or thirty people. This is a mandatory work training on diversity in the workplace. The participants are seated around a collection of conference tables formed into a horseshoe. The facilitator is standing at the front of the room. She is engaging as she shares information that is interesting and thought-provoking. She is determined to guide us toward stepping out of our individual and collective comfort zones.

We are several hours into the training. People are becoming more vulnerable. Everyone is learning, stretching and sharing. We are discussing current personal challenges so I take a full deep breath and stand up. I share a little of the story of my husband's stroke and speak of the aphasia that came as a result. I talk about his inability to speak and how I have essentially become his voice. I share how tired I am of speaking for my husband and how I am looking forward to the day when he will speak again and can take back his own voice. The instructor looks straight at me and gently asks, "And how will you get your voice back?"

I am stunned. I am completely speechless and just stand here staring at her. I feel the air leave the room. I feel my face flood with color, the heat slowly rising from my chest to my neck to my cheeks. I feel hot and sweaty and way too exposed. I take another deep breath and force myself not to cry. I don't say anything more and she doesn't push it.

The rest of the training flies by and I still can't get that question out of my head—"And how will you get your voice back?"

Now, looking back years later, I realize that was the first time I was consciously aware that my voice had taken a backseat. A spark was lit. An inquiry began and I stepped into the journey of reclaiming my authentic voice.

My Best Friend
May 2008 – Four Months After Stroke

I am back to work on intermittent family leave, doing some program development for the non-profit where I have worked for the past decade. I am grateful to be able to do some work from home as Tim and I ease back into some regular routines. It's been a rough four months since Tim's stroke and immersing myself in work gives me a socially appropriate break from the caregiving duties that have become my life. Given that my work also falls into the category of caregiving, the distraction is somewhat futile.

Today I am attending an all-day workshop at a conference center in the city where we live. The windowless conference room is large, with many tables spread throughout providing comfort for the participants as well as opportunities for small group discussions. The workshop is interesting and engaging, and it's a little surprising that I am able to concentrate. I am seated next to a colleague who is also a friend, and I'm delighted to be out of my house and back around people from work.

The event includes lunch, so my friend and I are catching up while eating. As I share the struggles and stress of the past few months, I savor the sense of being heard, being supported, being seen. I'm reminded of the camaraderie that exists in my workplace and realize just how much those connections mean to me.

"It sounds like you lost your best friend," my friend gently says to me. My eyes fill with tears and I feel them begin to fall, quietly hitting the napkin in my lap. The grief rolls over me like a wave as I sit here in a puddle of sadness. I have been primarily focused on Tim's losses related to the stroke—his loss of the ability to work, his loss of the ability to speak and understand language, his loss of independence, his loss of dignity. As I sit here crying in the presence of a wise friend, it slowly sinks in just how many significant losses have touched my life as well— namely the loss of my voice, the loss of my identity, the loss of my freedom. Those losses were somewhat obvious when I was thrown into the caregiver role. Until this very moment, at this table in this room of continuing education, it hadn't occurred to me that I also lost my best friend.

It's Not About the Root Beer
May 2008 – Four Months After Stroke

ike a couple in the romantic days of dating, Tim and I sit right next to each other at a table in one of our favorite brew pubs. We sit this way so we can talk more easily without having to raise our voices. Tim's voice is so quiet since having the stroke. It's a little noisy in here but the vibe is festive and friendly.

We've been eating dinner out in restaurants most nights since I returned to work, primarily to get Tim out of the house and also to give me a little break from the endless doing, doing, doing. Eating in restaurants is something we both enjoy and ordering food gives Tim the opportunity to practice speaking. It's a win-win situation that somehow makes life feel more normal.

We are looking at our menus and deciding what to order. I know he's not able to read most of what he sees, but holding a menu feels natural to him. Tim is practicing his words quietly under his breath. I tune him out and focus on what sounds good to eat. The server arrives to take our order. I go first, ordering a beet salad, a cup of soup, and an iced tea. Tim orders a French dip sandwich, a small salad, and a root beer. I am surprised when he says root beer as he *never* orders root beer. I ask him if he is sure he wants root beer. He is irritated by my question and snaps at me saying he wants root beer. I roll my eyes and focus on deep breathing.

The server brings the drinks. Tim takes a sip of his and angrily says. "This is root beer. I ordered Coke." I tell him he ordered root beer. He denies it. He's frustrated. I'm frustrated. This has become our communication dance. I find the server and order him a Coke.

The vibe is no longer festive and friendly.

Looking back many years later, this memory stands out as significant. Because of the stroke that was located right smack in the center of Tim's language center, he has aphasia—both receptive aphasia and expressive aphasia. What started out as minor annoyances in conversations eventually became huge hurdles in our marriage. Imagine thousands of challenging conversations where language is a barrier instead of a bridge. That was how our conversations played out for years, creating barriers that severely impacted our connection.

Reading for Answers
June 2008 – Five Months After Stroke

I sigh loudly as I close the book and drop it down on the coffee table. I just finished reading Jill Bolte Taylor's book *My Stroke of Insight: A Brain Scientist's Personal Journey* and I feel as confused as I was before I read it. Maybe more so. Everything she describes in the book about her stroke is light years away from what I know of Tim's. I am feeling really disheartened as I get up to get a sweatshirt to ward off the cooler evening air that always seems to seep into this old house when the sun goes down.

Memoirs and stories have always been my go-to way to learn, to feel seen, to feel connected. The few memoirs I've read about stroke have been relatable, but there isn't a single one I've read yet that feels like a warm blanket. The experience Ms. Bolte Taylor describes in her book is awful and beautiful and complex and amazing and her healing journey has been what many might describe as miraculous. I wonder if, years from now, we will look back on Tim's experience as awful but also beautiful. I have my doubts.

I look forward to having more conversations with Tim at some point about his internal experience of the stroke. I find myself wondering if he too felt a beautiful sense of calm during or after the stroke. When he was in the hospital for that first week I remember noticing his slow heart rate, his even breathing, and wondering why he didn't seem afraid or anxious—he seemed more confused than anything else.

I close my eyes and ask for peace, ask for healing, and ask for a memoir that will truly bring me some strokes of insight.

All these years later, Jill Bolte Taylor's second book Whole Brain Living: The Anatomy of Choice and the Four Characters That Drive Our Life *has been the best book I've ever read related to stroke and brain functioning. It has also helped Tim. I am so grateful for her willingness to share her story and her research. She has been a lifeline.*

Singing

June 2008 – Five Months After Stroke

Today Tim is going to sing a song. We are sitting in the small office of his speech therapist on a warm summer day. Tim has been coming here two to three times a week since his release from the hospital after the stroke. He continues to make progress on his expression of language and on understanding what he hears, but he still struggles to have even simple conversations.

He chose "Annie's Song" by John Denver to sing today, likely because it is a song that has been stored in his brain for decades. He's been practicing at home, but this is the first time I have heard him sing. Even though he starts out a little self-consciously, he relaxes after a few lines and sings the song with confidence.

"You fill up my senses..."

I am captivated, stunned into silence. His voice is fairly quiet but it is clear and steady and he sounds like himself. He pronounces each word accurately and is able to carry the tune. It is beautiful. The experience of truly feeling the presence of the old Tim is both strange and wonderful.

The therapist explains how music is stored in a different part of the brain—separate from the language center where Tim's stroke caused the most damage. He can sing what he can't say. Sadly, when he hears himself talk or sing, he still has no idea what is coming out of his mouth. His receptive aphasia is still wreaking havoc. He can still sing the ABCs but can't speak them or understand them. He can sing this lovely song but can't say the words unless he's singing. He still struggles to put a sentence together in conversation. It's astounding and heartbreaking and awe-inspiring, all at once.

When he talks, his voice is halting and broken.

When he sings, his voice is smooth and effortless.

When he sings, I can hear *him*. I can hear my husband.

Introductions
September 2008 – Eight Months After Stroke

Hanging out on our neighbor's front porch is such a great way to end the day. It's a beautiful fall evening and Tim and I are visiting with friends. It's relaxed and informal and we are enjoying ourselves. A woman arrives who I've not yet met, so I introduce myself. Tim introduces himself as well, using both his first and last name. I wince. It feels so formal. He isn't wrong, and yet his use of language feels wrong. The formality of it feels off for this particular situation. This has happened a number of times and I cringe each time. Language rules can be super subtle. They are quirky little things we pick up as kids and just *know* how to use. I wonder if I should say something.

This language situation reminds me of a time a decade or so ago when our neighbor's young daughter was learning to talk and she would address Tim by his name and then address me as "Timanddevon." When she would see us, she would yell "hi Tim, hi Timanddevon." It was the cutest damned thing and it always made me smile. Eventually she figured it out and started calling each of us by our own names.

Tim touches my arm and I come back to the present moment. I wonder what part of his brain is responsible for the ability to read and respond to social cues. I wonder if these neural pathways will come back or if he will have to relearn the rules for introductions.

I look over and smile at him, deciding not to say anything. Just like our neighbor's daughter, Tim will eventually figure it out. I am trusting his brain will heal and change.

Today, I am simply trusting.

Speaking Loudly

January 2009 – One Year After Stroke

I move the phone to my other ear and try not to look as bored as I feel. It's a typical Saturday. Tim and I are sitting facing each other on our sofa, talking on the phone with his parents who live out of state. We call from our landline so we can be on separate extensions, maximizing Tim's ability to process and understand the conversation. Tim's parents are also on two landline phones. We do this every week.

Tim talks, I translate.

Tim's parents talk, I translate.

I tend to do a lot of the talking, but, sadly, I am rarely "in" the conversations. I am talking, but it is not my life or thoughts that are being spoken about or heard. I have been encouraging Tim to talk more, in hopes of someday being relieved of this weekly duty.

At this moment Tim's dad is telling a story and it's clear from the look on Tim's face that he is getting confused. I give Tim an encouraging look and watch him finally speak up. "What?" he meekly says to his dad. ("What?" is what Tim says when he is confused, as "I don't understand what you are saying" is a whole lot of words to spit out at once.) His dad is now repeating exactly what he just said but this time MUCH MORE LOUDLY, as if saying it LOUDER will magically help Tim process and understand. His dad is clearly annoyed. Tim is annoyed. I roll my eyes and want to scream. Aphasia sucks.

I find myself wondering why we often speak to people who are old or disabled as if they are also deaf. I have listened to this repeatedly in the interactions people have had with Tim since his stroke. I also wonder what might be getting activated when people don't feel heard.

Maybe that also contributes to their speaking loudly with a tone of irritation. I can relate to both. Tim has said, "What?" to me so many times since his stroke and I feel irritation come up each and every time. I get it. I often lose my patience, loudly sigh, yell at him, or get frustrated and walk away. It's not pretty. I am just now learning to repeat what I've said much more slowly, in a slightly different way, and without the added tone or increased volume.

I tune back to the phone conversation and, while I can totally understand his dad's frustration, I still want to reach through the phone and slap him for speaking so rudely to Tim. I bite my tongue and say nothing. The conversation and translations go on. I emotionally check out, looking forward to the day when we can put all this behind us; looking forward to the day when we *both* can speak for ourselves.

Driving Lessons
January 2009 – One Year After Stroke

Tim turns the corner and I see headlights coming straight at us. Cars are honking, and I audibly gasp as a car swerves and barely avoids hitting our car. We are on the second level of a busy parking garage at a mall. The driving lanes and the parking spaces are clearly marked, some of them by concrete medians and some by painted lines. I quickly look over at Tim. He is stunned. I take a breath and slowly and succinctly tell him to move the car out of the lane of traffic and park. Tim accelerates and moves the car into an open space. We both sit here frozen as he fully comprehends that he was driving the *wrong way* down a one-way roadway, and we were almost hit in a head-on collision. It also sinks in that he didn't maneuver the car out of the way when the car was coming at us—he didn't do anything to avoid a collision. Thankfully, the other driver was able to avoid hitting us.

It's been about a year since Tim's stroke, and he's been itching to get behind the wheel and back on the road again. His doctor supported his request to drive but with some conditions—he can only drive during the day, to places he knows, and with me in the car. Lucky me.

I've been taking him driving, which has been challenging and probably not unlike teaching a teenager how to drive. His confidence in his ability to drive far exceeds his actual ability. He knows *how* to drive, but his brain is taking in thousands of bits of information all at once, and he's processing this information at a much slower rate than before. Reading street signs, moving the hands and feet, calculating distances from other cars as well as the distance from the middle and sides of the road, watching the speedometer while watching for other cars and pedestrians. All of these combine to create a pretty complex mental challenge for someone recovering from a brain injury. His depth perception is completely off, and he drives way too close to other cars. His anxiety makes him irritable and not very amenable to directions from his nagging wife. I say a lot of prayers when he gets behind the wheel.

Tim and I wordlessly switch places in the car. We are both shaking and too freaked out to even say anything. I have been giving him advice and feedback for weeks, all of which he has quickly brushed off and ignored.

This time, it registers.

He's not yet ready to be driving.

It's simply not safe.

Panic in the Car
January 2009 – One Year After Stroke

I am driving north in rush-hour traffic to a massage appointment. It's early evening on a cold winter day and it's already dark outside. In front of me I see lines of taillights of cars and trucks on the freeway. I am driving along in the right lane, watchful and paying attention. I see cars merging from the on-ramp on my right. I look to move left, but there are cars in the middle lane, leaving me unable to move out of the right lane. I speed up to get out of the way of a black sedan that is coming my way from the on-ramp. I continue in the right lane and then see headlights in my rear-view mirror that look like they are inches from my bumper. I feel the adrenalin start to course through my body. I am now on high alert. The person in the car behind me flashes their brights, continuing to ride my bumper as I cross the Interstate Bridge and head into Vancouver, Washington.

I signal and take my exit. The black car continues to follow, then goes around me on my left and gets in front of me and slows down. I can see it's a man driving the car. He's flipping me off. I wonder why he is so aggressive. I hang back. He pulls over off the road to the right. I breathe a sigh of relief and hope it's over. It's not. He gets back on the road behind me and continues to flash his lights and ride my bumper. I keep driving. I am getting close to my destination but decide not to stop in front of the building, feeling way too vulnerable.

I drive to a stoplight and pull out my phone and call 911. I am shaking and afraid. The man pulls up on my right and when he sees me on the phone, he yells something I don't understand, takes a quick right turn, and speeds off down the road. I can't stop shaking. I give the police my name and information and a description of the car and driver and end the call.

I circle back and drive to the building where I am scheduled to have my massage appointment. I sit in my car for about fifteen minutes, breathing and shaking and trying to calm down. I want to call my husband, but I don't know what to say. I don't know how to convey how scared I am and how alone I feel. The distance between us feels insurmountable right now. Tim won't understand. He will get frustrated because he can't understand my words and then I will be frustrated with him for not understanding.

It's a vicious cycle. I also don't want to worry him. I have gotten really good at hiding and minimizing my distress. It seems to come naturally with my new role as a caregiver. I don't know what to do, so I do nothing. I take a deep breath and get out of the car, checking up and down the street for black sedans. I go into my massage appointment, downplay the incident, and apologize for being late. I basically suck it up.

My massage therapist assumes I am stressed due to work and the traffic that may have made me late for the appointment. I don't correct her. I play along. I am afraid if I say what happened, I will start crying and never be able to stop. It's easier to just stuff it down. If she knows something more is going on, she doesn't push it, which is a relief. The massage is helpful, and I am able to stop shaking and feel myself relax a little. It seems ironic, even to me, that the act of going to a massage just created significantly more stress in my life.

I drive home on high alert after my massage, cautiously watching for a black sedan. I am still a little shaky and pretty freaked out when I get home. Tim is sitting at the dining room table eating a sandwich. He looks up and says hello. He doesn't even notice my distress. I blink back the tears and say nothing. I skip dinner and go straight to bed, feeling so unspeakably lonely. As I drift off to sleep, I realize that some- times trauma happens in the moment when our loved ones suffer an injury and sometimes trauma happens in various random moments that come after.

All these years later, I still have a panic response when someone drives too close to me on a freeway. Because of the crazy ride in the ambulance after Tim's stroke and that incident on the freeway, I am not able to relax when driving or riding in a car. I have learned to ask friends and family members to slow down when I feel activated, but my primary way of dealing with it is to always be the driver and avoid freeways as much as possible.

Scraps of Love

February 2009 – One Year and One Month After Stroke

I finish cleaning up the kitchen and walk down the hall, pausing in the doorway to the living room. The house is quiet, and Tim is sitting on the couch looking through a scrapbook for probably the hundredth time. I stand there watching, smiling, feeling his energy change as he taps into just how much love and support exists for him.

Because Tim wasn't able to read or understand much in the first few months after the stroke, I gathered up all of the cards and letters he received and then printed out all the supportive emails and texts that came his way. I put them all in a scrapbook so that one day, when he was better, he would know just how much he was loved. I had no idea how much it would impact him.

The container of friends and family is a gift. The meals, the visits, the cards and letters and messages, and the phone calls. These are all gifts as well. My offering was to gather and glue the gifts into a book of healing support.

Tim closes the book and smiles. He sets it on the coffee table and turns to see me standing in the doorway. There is a look that passes between us.

A silent look of gratitude for this gift.

A silent look of gratitude for a scrapbook filled with love.

On Guard at the Airport
May 2009 – One Year and Four Months After Stroke

The waiting line goes on for what seems like forever, and—poof!— just like that, my vacation buzz is gone. We are heading home after a couple of beautiful, relaxing weeks in Belize. First stop, Houston Airport Customs and Immigration. Several large planes came in at the same time and there are about a thousand folks in front of us. Literally. This is going to suck.

Conversation is pretty much out of the question, due to my husband's aphasia. This leaves people-watching and sleepwalking as my two best options for passing the time, neither of which is on the list of how I want to end a wonderful vacation. I sleepwalk and remember very little of our experience in line. Did I mention how much I hate airports?

Bored and irritable, we finally make it to the podium after a couple of hours in line. I can almost smell freedom, even though I am quite sure we have missed our connecting flight. You might say I am primed to have things go wrong, horribly wrong.

The agent, a man about our age, who looks about as bored as we are, blandly asks for our passports. It reminds me of assembly-line work, and we are many widgets down the line. He swipes my passport and hands it back without even looking up. After swiping Tim's passport, his eyes light up, he perks up considerably, and he starts drilling my husband with lots of questions. There are about a zillion people who share Tim's first and last name and at least one of them has done something very, very, bad. We get stopped and detained and searched and questioned upon return to the US every single time we travel outside of the country. We have come to expect it and usually just go through the motions until eventually they figure out he is not *that* very bad person, and off we go.

This time—the second time since my husband's stroke and subsequent aphasia—is different, dramatically different. Tim can't say his birthdate or where he lives or where he works or his social security number. He knows the answers but cannot find the words. I am sure the immigration agent is confused and therefore alarmed, as Tim is young and fit and tan and has no visible signs of any disability, and yet he can't answer the most basic questions about himself. Red flags all over the place.

I jump in, explaining that Tim had a stroke and has aphasia, but I am abruptly cut off by the now testy immigration agent. He tells me to be quiet and asks me to leave. He actually makes a shooing motion as if I'm a fly, an irritant at his desk. He keeps my husband's passport and ushers him to an aisle nearby, where he is joined by two heavily armed guards. I follow them. I won't leave Tim. I stick like glue. They keep loudly saying, "Ma'am, you need to leave." I am so pissed off and protective and just keep loudly saying, "No." I am yelling that my husband has aphasia due to a stroke and has difficulty speaking and I WILL NOT LEAVE HIM. I am not going to leave him.

I become *that crazy lady at the airport*. Even though there are many agents with many guns surrounding me, I am not budging. I am now a *situation* that needs to be fixed. I guess they figure shooting a hysterical wife who won't leave her possibly disabled husband in a room full of hundreds of travelers might not be a good idea after all, and they escort us, both of us, to a locked holding room—a jail of sorts for naughty travelers.

After many more questions and what seems like hours and much more irritation at having missed our flight, an official returns Tim's passport to him and cheerfully says, "Welcome back to the US." No apology. No explanation. No empathy. I want to slap the shit out of him but settle for giving him a very dirty look. It doesn't faze him.

We are finally let out of our holding pen and, like good little American citizens, we move along to wait in yet another line that appears to go on forever.

The vacation buzz is now most definitely gone.

The Ungodly B & B
July 2009 – One Year and Six Months After Stroke

I have a love-hate relationship with bed and breakfasts. I love that I can take a peek into someone else's life in a pro-social way and satisfy my never-ending curiosity of people's quirks, and I dread that I might actually have to talk to or interact with strangers. So here I am, in the early morning on a beautiful summer day in Central Oregon, seated at a table with a bunch of strangers and a husband who still struggles to speak and understand language. What the hell?

I tilt my head back and feel the warmth of the sun on my face. I close my eyes, briefly allowing the world to fade away. I smell the pancakes and bacon and breathe deeper to smell the coffee and the juniper bushes nearby. *I can do this. I can do this.*

We are spending a long weekend at a bed and breakfast to decompress and celebrate Tim's progress in his recovery from the stroke. As with all B & B experiences, we share the place with a cast of characters that one would never imagine throwing together. There is the young couple who spent their honeymoon hiking the Pacific Crest Trail. They are spending the tail-end of their trip at the bed and breakfast to transition themselves back to reality and get the stink off. I'm pretty sure if you look up "Honeymoon from Hell" on the Internet, the description will match their experience: no showers, sleeping on the ground, eating crap food, lots of hungry mosquitoes, blisters, body odor, etc. Surprisingly, at least to me, they appear happy, really happy. They are interesting and idealistic and tell some great stories. Breakfast is going pretty well so far.

Another couple at the table is a little younger than us and are pregnant with their first child. Since we are in the process of adopting our first child, I fall into some easy expectant-parent conversations with them. Tim seems a little relieved to sit back and listen and not get asked any direct questions. We eat amazing food and things feel sort of normal. Feeling normal is not the norm for us at this time in our lives. It is an unusually pleasant morning thus far.

The other couple in our odd little collection of folks is from out-of-state and possibly straight out of the 1960s: very hippie and very fascinating—quirky with a capital Q. This is going to be fun. The woman claims she is a doctor, but of what it isn't clear, and she doesn't fully disclose. Her partner is a massage therapist and they describe a living situation that sounds a little like an ashram in a remote area of Colorado. After asking the usual questions regarding where you live and what you do, etc., I start blathering on about our recent life-changing events and how we are coping. I am always looking for any little tidbits of advice from those in the medical community—anything that might improve Tim's recovery journey. I wonder if she is really a doctor, as her comments sound less informed about strokes than mine, which is a little disturbing because I consider myself to be pretty clueless in this area. I also wonder if maybe she has smoked a little too much weed in her lifetime.

Tim appears to be following the conversation with this eccentric couple and seems interested in their responses, so I continue to throw questions at them and ramble on about our lives. The massage therapist then takes a philosophical turn and starts waxing on about his belief that all things happen for a reason and that all events can always be looked at as positive experiences. Typically, this is pretty normal stuff and not that different from my beliefs, but in our fairly new and tender situation, this is fuel for a very unpredictable fire. My anxiety shoots through the roof and I think, *Uh oh*. The massage therapist then turns and directly asks Tim what gift God has given him through this experience. My husband, a devout atheist, with aphasia, looks the guy straight in the eye and says, *"Fuck God!"* His eyes are angry, and his voice is clear and loud. I silently cheer him on and watch as all the couples quickly excuse themselves from our presence.

Look who's quirky now.

Getting to Work
July 2009 – One Year and Six Months After Stroke

t's dark and raining as I wait in my car on a side street near the train station. Tim called from his cell phone about ten minutes ago and let me know he would be at the station soon. This is our new routine.

Tim has been back to work for a few weeks. Since driving takes a ton of mental energy and he works eighteen miles from our home, he's been taking the train and then walking the last mile from the train station to his work. It's more than an hour and a half door to door twice a day when he works. Currently he is working four hours per week. That's not a typo—it's only four hours per week. He goes in one day a week and works a half day. It's a bitch of a commute for a very short workday, but he doesn't care. He is over the moon to be back in the office.

Tim has been putting all of his energy into getting back to work, getting back to coding, and getting back to being a part of the tech world. I watched him power through endless hurdles and setbacks and roadblocks and I know how much he wants this chance. If he didn't, he would have thrown in the towel a long, long time ago.

I look in my rear-view mirror and see him crossing the street behind me. I recognize his gait, which is a little bit different than it was before. Being paralyzed on one side of the body, even for a short time, leaves a mark. He's wearing a backpack containing his laptop and has his dark umbrella up. I notice how he seems really tired and ten-feet-tall all at the same time. He gets in the car and tells me he will be adding another four-hour shift starting next week. He's so happy. I blink back happy tears as I put on my turn signal and the windshield wipers. I slowly pull away from the curb and head toward home.

Today, not even the rain can rain on our parade.

The Power of Play

September 2009 – One Year and Eight Months After Stroke

The sunshine dances as it filters through the trees. Tim and I are at a small community park a few blocks from our home. It's a beautiful fall day and we are outside enjoying it. The park isn't too busy today, with only a couple of families over by the swings. Thankfully, we have this corner of the park to ourselves. So much of Tim's focus lately has been on communication—speaking, writing, and reading. Today the focus is on adding sports back into his world, not just as an observer but as a fully active participant.

Engaging in sports has always been important to Tim, especially when done with one or more friends. He is such a social guy. Tennis, skiing, basketball, flag football, running, hiking, scuba diving, swimming, and biking are some of his favorites. He even tried skydiving once but promised me he wouldn't do that again. I used to tease him that if Scottish log-rolling were available in our city, he'd be doing that too. Tim also likes to watch sports on TV, but if the choices were to participate, watch something live, or watch on TV, he would always choose to participate or watch live. Our past fifteen years together has included countless fun trips to ballgames in Seattle, diving vacations in the Caribbean, and what we called "summer camp" at a vacation resort in central Oregon where we would spend a week every summer biking, hiking, swimming, and playing tennis.

Today we are at the park playing catch with a football. We started tossing the football in our backyard, but our yard is fairly small and we needed more space, so we walked to the closest park. Because Tim was paralyzed on his right side for a few days following the stroke, his right hand (his dominant hand) was impacted. He can throw with his right hand but it's wildly inconsistent, which leads to much frustration. He is now focused on learning to throw with his left hand. His coordination with his right hand will improve over time, but his left hand will likely be easier to train right now so that is his plan. He throws the ball to me and I catch it and throw it back. Over and over and over. His spiral is a little wobbly at first but quickly improves.

Within a short amount of time, he is actually throwing the ball pretty well with his left hand.

Within a short amount of time, we forget why we're doing what we're doing and we actually start laughing and having a little fun, enjoying the sunshine that dances through the trees.

On Being a Dad
December 2009 – One Year and Eleven Months After Stroke

I'm nervous and shaking a little as I watch the clock on the wall. Tim and I sit in a small exam room at our primary care physician's office. We have been in one of these exam rooms so many times since the stroke. Once Tim was released from the hospital, his case was primarily turned over to his PCP and though most of his actual "care" has been handled elsewhere, we have been here many times to have forms signed for medical leave, disability insurance, and Social Security applications. I often wonder how a doctor can have time for patients when there is so much paperwork to be done.

In this exam room there is a large window in the wall across from the door. The view is obscured by cheap plastic blinds, which are closed to provide privacy from the busy outside world. The sunshine is streaming in on both sides of the blinds, reminding us of the beautiful day that is happening outside. Tim is fully clothed and sitting on the exam table. I am sitting in the lone black plastic chair under the window. My body is humming with anxiety as we wait. I look up as our friendly and deeply caring doctor comes in and sits down on a stool with wheels and quickly rolls over to sit between us. He's always in a hurry and yet he always takes the time to answer all of our questions and leaves us feeling hopeful before he runs off to his next patient.

We both had worked with this doctor for several years before Tim's stroke, primarily for things like sore throats or annual physicals. He was also the one who performed the necessary slew of tests for getting approval to adopt internationally. It's been a comfort in the weeks and months after the stroke to work with someone who knew Tim before his brain injury—someone who knew how far Tim had fallen and how hard he has worked to find his way back. Our doctor was as surprised as we were when the stroke occurred. It made absolutely no sense for someone as healthy as Tim to have had a major stroke.

I tell the doctor that we believe we are ready to move forward with adopting a child. We are here to get his blessing and a signed document stating that we are both fit to adopt. We have completed many, many tests over the past few years in preparation for this step. The stroke was a major glitch in the process, but we believe we are now ready to throw our hat back in the ring. Our doctor looks at us as if we are crazy. I feel my heart drop into my stomach and hold my breath. He stands up, waves his arms, and emphatically says, "Of course you two are fit to adopt." He seems surprised that we would even doubt our ability to move forward. He looks at us and says emphatically, "There is no physical reason that Tim couldn't be a great dad." Those words resonate over and over as we sit here and smile.

The doctor completes the necessary forms and notes Tim's prognosis as "excellent."

Tim walks out of the clinic clutching the medical reports, excited and filled with the hope of really getting his life back.

I walk out of there beaming, certain we have finally turned the corner. We are putting this hell behind us and are moving toward a distinctly brighter future.

Partnering as New Parents
May 2010 – Two Years and Three Months After Stroke

The sound of conversations and the smell of yummy food fill the bustling little café. Tim and I are enjoying a leisurely breakfast at one of our favorite neighborhood restaurants. It's a sunny spring Saturday morning. We are seated at a cozy little table for two under a window, talking, eating delicious food, and relishing the weekend break from our busy jobs.

My phone rings. When I see it is our adoption coordinator calling, I quickly answer and rush outside to be better able to hear her voice. She tells me our daughter is about to be born. *Oh my God! Our daughter is about to be born.* The hospital is about five hours away and it's time for me and Tim to get on the road and go. I let the coordinator know we will be on our way as soon as possible and end the call.

I rush back in and tell Tim the news. We are both ecstatically happy and scared out of our minds. We are about to become parents for the first time. I'm buzzing with energy and shaking as I flag down our server and pay the bill. We rush out of there to head home, pack up, and hit the road—hoping to be there in time for our daughter's birth.

We have been packing for the past week and everything is pretty much ready to go. We know we may be out of town for a while, as she is being born in another state. There are strict rules about not crossing any state lines with a baby following adoption placement until the proper documents are filed with a court. Our attorney let us know this could take up to a week. We reserved a room at a hotel that was willing to hold a room for us. We throw the suitcases, the car seat, the portable crib, and a whole lot of unnecessary baby gear into the car and head north, briefly stopping for gas and snacks on the way out of town.

Tim drives as I make phone calls and send emails.

I feel partnered.

I am not alone in this.

Today we are becoming parents and we are doing it together.

Bonding

June 2010 – Two Years and Five Months After Stroke

Our daughter is fussy and tired, which means I am also fussy and tired. She screams if I put her down, needing to always be touching and be touched. Our daughter is two months old and is such a tactile baby. I am not one to let her cry it out. She needs what she needs, and she is great at expressing those needs. I am her mama, so I know it is my job to respond to her needs even when I am fussy and tired. She is crying loudly now, and I am certain walking with her would be soothing, but I am so beyond exhausted. I resign myself to simply holding her and loudly whispering "Shhhhhhh" in her ear. It helps a little.

I hear footsteps and look up from the couch and smile with relief as Tim walks toward us. He gently takes our daughter from me, settles her into his arms, and starts walking back and forth from the dining room to the living room. He holds her tenderly and looks at her sweet face, cooing softly at her as she slowly drifts to sleep. I am moved and so overwhelmingly grateful to be in a marriage where we can do this parenting journey together. It's hard to imagine the level of exhaustion I'd be experiencing if I were a single parent. I shake my head, willing those thoughts away.

Our daughter is amazing and delightful in so many ways, but the sleep issue has been rough. She has motion sickness, so swings and car rides are out of the question. They are agony for her and for us. She has been sleeping at night in a bassinet next to our bed but will only stay asleep if I rest my hand on her at all times. I know it is only a matter of time until she ends up sleeping in our bed. She only falls asleep if someone is holding her, which has led to lots of parent and child naps in the living room and some rather interesting comments from those who claim to love us. I'm too fussy and tired to give a shit.

I wake up on the couch, realizing I too must have drifted off to sleep. Tim is sitting in a chair across from me with our sleeping baby in his arms. I smile at him and slowly pull myself up to get on with the day, feeling that deep sense of contentment that comes when you know someone truly has your back.

Happy Dad, Happy Baby
July 2010 – Two Years and Six Months After Stroke

I smile at the delight on our daughter's face as she takes in the scenery. Tim and I are strolling with Tim's parents through a beautiful park near our home enjoying the variety of trees and the lovely summer weather. Tim is carrying our three-month-old in a BabyBjörn, a carrier that is quite popular right now. She loves it—but only if she is facing away from the human who is carrying her. She is completely fascinated by the world.

We visit with each other as we meander through the park and I feel an ease with Tim's parents that hasn't been there since the stroke. It's as if they have stopped worrying so much about Tim's health and have finally stepped into the role of doting grandparents.

When we first shared with Tim's parents our plans to adopt a child, they were only mildly supportive and expressed some concerns about us being "older" parents. I could clearly hear the concern in their voices. We welcomed their concerns, assured them that we weren't taking it lightly, and then forged ahead on the path that felt best for us. When the stroke happened, we put our parenting plans on hold and then, as Tim's health improved, we dusted off our plan and decided to move forward and adopt a child.

Tim's parents, who live in Colorado, have been here for a few days and it's been a lovely experience. They met our baby girl. They have seen with their own eyes how well Tim is doing and they have visibly relaxed. I walk ahead and then turn around and snap another photo of Tim with his parents and our daughter. Three generations. Wow. The smiles on their faces say it all. They are all so happy. His parents are so relieved. We are all basking in the light of family.

Defying the Odds
July 2010 – *Two Years and Six Months After Stroke*

It's a beautiful day—sunny and warm with a light, comfortable breeze. Perfect summer weather. Tim and I are standing side by side on the concrete steps of a building at Portland State University. We are chatting with a couple of researchers and basking in the warmth of the conversation and the sun. We are so full of hope. We are also armored up with a sense of resolve, determined to defy the odds and beat this thing called a brain injury.

A few months ago, a graduate student from the School of Social Work at Portland State gave a presentation at a stroke support group we attended. The student was looking for couples to be interviewed. He talked about a study that was being done at the University to learn how survivors and their committed partners cope after stroke, focusing primarily on the depressive symptoms of both the survivor and the caregiver. The researchers were also gathering information in the study related to the relationship, outlooks on the future, coping strategies, expectations of each other, and the mental health of both partners. We quickly volunteered to be interviewed.*

Now, we are all in. It has been two and a half years since Tim's stroke and we are living in a self-made bubble of optimism and are happy to share our success story with anyone who will listen.

I look around us at the campus, taking a moment to feel the sun on my skin. I feel *special*. I feel confident. I believe Tim and I are *special* because, for some reason, Tim survived a brain injury that sometimes kills people. I believe we are *special* because our marriage survived an experience that sometimes destroys relationships. I am relieved and, frankly, I am feeling a little bit entitled, a little bit untouchable. Maybe after all the challenges of the past couple of years our lives can finally go back to being blessed.

We finished up our interviews about an hour ago and are now sharing even more about our success story with some curious graduate students. It really is a beautiful story. The conversation feels more friendly than formal. Tim has greatly improved in all areas of life and our lives are returning to some sort of normal. He is physically healthy, his speech has greatly improved, he is driving, he's been back to work for a year, and we just adopted our first child. We *are* blessed.

A graduate student is sharing about some of the statistics that compelled the researchers to take on this area of study. My mouth drops open when I hear a couple of the statistics: 1) The divorce rate of married couples after a spouse is diagnosed with aphasia may be even higher than the already appallingly high divorce rate, and 2) caregivers may actually be more likely to struggle with depression than stroke survivors.

These ideas are shocking to me, even after the journey we've been on. I wonder what would have happened if Tim hadn't gotten better. Would we have become a statistic? I wonder about people without the resources and privileges that were available to us. Tim was a leader in his field and was given an *indefinite* leave of absence from his work. We weren't worried about whether or not he would have a job to go back to. We weren't worried about losing our health insurance. We weren't worried about bankruptcy or losing our home. We were able to put a significant amount of time and energy toward healing. How differently this may have played out if he didn't have a job or the resources for healing. I take this all in and then slowly tuck away the discomfort, shoving it way in the back of my mind, out of sight, out of reach, out of conscious awareness.

I focus on the present moment and this conversation with these researchers. I smile. I take Tim's hand. We are united. I believe our love and the strength of our marriage will get us through anything.

I am naively determined to defy the odds.

Researcher: Michael J. McCarthy, MSW, PhD. Results of the study published online 31 Jul 2012.

True Thanksgiving
November 2010 – Two Years and Ten Months After Stroke

It's Thanksgiving Day, our first Thanksgiving since becoming parents, and this year I am actually feeling thankful. I am hosting a family gathering and it feels different. Really different. I feel settled in a way that hasn't been available to me in many years. Things are looking up. Tim is doing well at work. Our daughter is about six months old. I am getting more comfortable with being a mom and I am feeling hopeful for the future.

I stand in the space between the living and dining rooms, directing family members to stand together to get their photos taken. I have pulled out my good camera and am excited to get some great shots. Tim is holding our daughter in a BabyBjörn carrier, and she is smiling at anyone who pays her any attention. She is having a blast. Tim is smiling and laughing. I capture photos of my mom, her husband, my brother, and my nephew—all wearing huge smiles and laughing at the baby or some inside joke. I am delighted.

After taking a ton of photos—thank you, digital camera—the guys all move to be closer to the TV to watch some football. Tim is holding our daughter on his lap. I smile happily as I clear the table and look over at my husband. He seems so happy. I can clearly see him coming back to me. I send up a blessing of gratitude. Today I understand what being truly thankful feels like.

Our First Little Family Christmas
December 2010 – Two Years and Eleven Months After Stroke

Pure delight radiates from our daughter. Each time her hand connects with the drum and makes a sound, she lights up with a big smile. Her laughter and joy are infectious. She is sitting in front of Tim with a drum in front of her. The drum is almost as big as she is and she pounds on it with her hands then eagerly leans down to put her mouth on it. It's Christmas Day and we are sitting on the living room rug with our eight-month-old daughter. It's her first Christmas—our first Christmas as parents. Tim and I marvel at the simple joy this brings to both of us.

This year, we have done all the new-parent things—taken our daughter to see Santa (which she hated), went on a Christmas river cruise (which she loved), had family photos taken with our daughter in a fancy red dress, bought her a hat that reads *My First Christmas*, and we now have three red velvet stockings hanging from the fireplace mantel instead of two. Of all the things we've done, this morning in our living room with our daughter and the drum has been the highlight. It really is the simple things.

It's been almost three years since Tim had his stroke and the joy has definitely come back into our lives. Moments like this remind me that whatever we have walked through already, or will walk through in the future, parenting may be our biggest source of delight.

Daddy's Home
March 2011 – Three Years and Two Months After Stroke

I glance out the window for the hundredth time. It's dinnertime on a Friday night and I am in the dining room with our ten-month-old daughter, watching and waiting for Tim to get home from work. He called a while ago and said he was on his way. He should be here soon. Dinner is ready and our daughter is hungry, but I'm hoping she can wait a little longer so we can all eat together.

As I stare out the front window, my mind drifts back to a day about six months ago when we met with our adoption coordinator to let him know we wanted to move forward with adopting a second child. We had been on a waiting list to adopt a child from China for about four years and had decided we were ready to grow our family, ready to bring home a sibling for our daughter. We weren't sure it was the best decision, but our hearts were saying yes so we took the plunge and started the process.

I now see headlights coming up the driveway and bring my attention back to the here and now. I pick up my daughter so she can watch out the window. We watch as Tim gets out of the car and retrieves his backpack from the backseat. He turns and waves to us in the window and heads for the front door. As he walks through the door, our daughter's face brightens and she puts on a smile that lights up the room. She tries to wiggle out of my arms, wanting to be put down to crawl to him. I take her over to him and she grabs onto him and nuzzles into his neck, but only for a second. She pulls back so she can resume her grinning and looking at him. It is so sweet to watch. He may not be her biological father but he is most certainly her dad.

In this moment, I am absolutely sure we made the right decision to move forward with our second adoption.

U-Haul Adventure
May 2011 – Three Years and Four Months After Stroke

After a day of driving that has taken twice as many hours as expected, I finally cross the border into Oregon. It's only Day One of our road trip home from central California and it's been a long one. Our one-year-old daughter is blissfully asleep in the backseat after spending most of the day crying and screaming. I am driving in our silver four-door sedan with our daughter, and Tim is up ahead, driving a small U-Haul truck carrying some large items that were given to us by my dad. It's getting dark and the temperature is dropping as the road starts to climb up onto Mt. Ashland. I am so grateful and relieved that it's finally quiet in the car.

As I continue to drive up the mountain, I see snowflakes starting to hit my windshield. *Shit.* I don't see that well in the dark. Driving at night in an unexpected snowstorm with my baby in the backseat is not a great situation. I take a few deep breaths and consciously loosen my grip on the steering wheel. Thank God there isn't any noise to add to my anxiety. What is helping me in this moment is seeing the taillights of the U-Haul truck in front of me, driven by my competent and very calm husband. He is driving slowly which I appreciate. I wonder if maybe the U-Haul truck can't go any faster up a hill, but it doesn't matter. I am grateful, nonetheless. I breathe, release my tight grip on the steering wheel and say little calming mantras to myself. *I can do this. I am held. I am not alone. Keep my eyes on the lights. Tim will get us there safely.*

Tim is quite literally my calm in the midst of a snowstorm.

It's now Day Two of our road trip home from central California. After spending the night in Ashland, Oregon, we are back on the road and heading for home. I am driving north on Interstate 5 near Eugene. Our daughter is in the backseat of the car, facing the back of the car, screaming at the top of her lungs. Tim is up ahead of me in the U-Haul truck. Our daughter has been screaming for several hours and I am losing my ever-loving mind. I have pulled over multiple times to check on her and, even though I know she is safe, it breaks my heart to hear her in such distress. She is in a rear-facing car seat for her safety and she is alone in the back seat. Quite the recipe for disaster. On the way to California a week ago, Tim and I drove in the car together so one of us was always able to sit in the back with her, which made the trip pleasant and kind of fun. This two-day trip back to Northern Oregon has not been pleasant or fun.

I pull out my cell phone and call Tim, whining to him about the hell I am experiencing. He can't hear me over the crying from the back seat, but it doesn't matter. It feels better to hear his voice and know we are in this thing together. I continue to talk, hoping maybe my voice will soothe my screaming daughter and hoping Tim's voice will bring some much-needed distraction as the miles fly by.

Today, Tim's voice is the calm in the midst of a different kind of storm.

Holding Those We Love
July 2011 – Three Years and Six Months After Stroke

Traveling with a baby is always an adventure in patience and humility. It's summertime and we are visiting Tim's parents in Colorado. We have been here for a couple of days and are slowly getting acclimated to the altitude and to the dual role of being parents and children in the same space. Our daughter is just over a year old and we are getting used to parenting as she gets used to being a human in this world. She is a busy, talkative kid who loves to play and explore. She loves attention, and having four doting adults in the home brings her a tremendous amount of joy.

It's early afternoon and we are all sitting in the living room visiting. It's pleasant, a nice break from a busy morning at a park. Tim is sitting on a sofa holding our daughter as she naps. She is one of those kids who needs to be touching someone, needs to be held. Holding her until she falls asleep works best for her. We have decided to honor her need rather than try to break it out of her. Listening to her cry incessantly doesn't serve her or anyone else. It's very clear from the look on Tim's parents' faces that they are not supportive of our parenting choices. His mom finally speaks up and says to Tim, "Put that baby down!" I am shocked and a little sad. I look to him to see what he will do. Tim gently says to his parents that this is how our daughter sleeps best, so when he is able to hold her, he will. I am so appreciative of him in this moment.

I close my eyes, take a deep breath and send some compassion to Tim and to his parents. I get a glimpse into how Tim was raised—probably how our whole generation was raised—and I am grateful we are breaking this particular cycle. So many of our choices over the years since the stroke, and probably throughout our lives, have been about how we choose to hold, and be held by, those we love.

Fun on the Freeway
January 2012 – Three Years and Eleven Months After Stroke

I am bleary-eyed, exhausted, and dragging. It is still dark, just a couple of hours before sunrise, as we fly into the airport in Beijing a long, long twelve hours after leaving Vancouver, BC. My husband and baby daughter managed to sleep most of the way, but I stayed awake, having always struggled with sleeping while sitting upright in noisy places surrounded by a bunch of strangers. Call me crazy. We are on our way to China for a few weeks to visit family and adopt our second child—a baby the same age as our daughter, who was adopted at birth in the U.S. less than two years ago. Virtual twins. Call me crazy again. I am extremely excited, but at this moment I am mostly just bleary-eyed, exhausted, and want to get where we are going. First stop in the Beijing airport: Starbucks.

My cousin meets us at the airport to help us navigate our way into the city. That should have been a sign or an omen of some kind. Why would someone need to meet us at the airport to help us get to a hotel? We have traveled to many foreign countries and usually manage just fine. Beijing, a city of roughly twenty million people, is far bigger than what I can imagine in terms of size, so I humored my cousin and agreed to his offer to help us.

First hurdle: Family of three—soon to be four—traveling to China for three weeks equals three large suitcases, a stroller, a diaper bag, and two large backpacks. We think we're traveling light. As we head out of the airport with all of our belongings to catch a taxi, I am stunned to see that all the taxis are small, really small, like the smallest four-door sedans you can imagine. Where are the big cars, the vans, the SUVs?

We are a group of three adults (including my cousin, who taxied out to the airport to meet us), a baby, and all our first-world gear. The trunk in each of the sedans will hold only one suitcase. We are screwed.

We decide to split up—my husband and all the luggage in one car, and my cousin, my daughter, and I in the other. Let the comedy show begin. My cousin, an American who has lived in China for more than a decade, is trying to communicate our desired destination to both drivers. Basically, he shows both drivers the address of the hotel, and off we go. One driver appears to understand and the other driver uses the word for *follow*. It's not clear if anyone really understands anything. We set off in our little convoy of two little cars and hit the big freeway.

Nothing could have prepared me for this experience. I am not prepared for the near-death crazy driving that happens here *all the time*. There are no seatbelts, no car seat for the baby, and evidently no rules for the road. Well, maybe one rule—try not to die. We are on a freeway with five lanes heading into the city and there are eight lanes of cars across it. We are going so fast and driving so close to the cars on both sides of us. I feel like I am in a movie or a bad dream. My cousin informs me that most expatriates who live in Beijing hire professional drivers rather than drive themselves. (I'm picturing NASCAR drivers in full gear.)

Holy shit.

After taking more than a few deep breaths, I realize the sun is starting to rise and Tim, my beloved husband with global aphasia, is in a taxi in a city of close to twenty million people and he speaks no Mandarin, struggles at times to speak or understand English, does not have the address of our hotel, has a cell phone that doesn't work in China, and his cab driver is trying to *follow* us on this freeway from hell. I start frantically searching for the other car, which looks like every other small, dark four-door sedan on the road. Then I see him. He is *in front* of us. I know it is him because he is tall, Caucasian, and I can see his green University of Oregon ball cap. I start yelling. My cousin is trying to relay this information to the driver in broken Mandarin. The driver is honking and weaving in and out of traffic, following the guy who is supposed to be following us. We are flying around in the backseat and my daughter is crying and I am just absolutely certain we are all going to die.

Surprisingly, we don't.

After many near accidents, we manage to pass the other car and get the driver's attention. Somehow, an hour later, we arrive safely at our hotel, our place of respite for the next week. Time to finally get some much-needed rest.

The only problem—I have never been so awake in my entire life.

Paternity Leave
February 2012 – Four Years After Stroke

I feel a pang of sadness at the change that is coming. It's a weekday morning and we are sitting at our dining room table having break-fast. Our daughters are in highchairs, one next to me and one next to Tim, on opposite sides of the table. We've been back from China for a couple of weeks and today Tim is returning to work after taking about six weeks off for paternity leave following the adoption of our second child. It's been a wild ride. We spent a few weeks in China traveling, visiting family who live there, and getting to know our newly adopted daughter, while traveling to three major cities with two one-year-olds. It was quite an experience.

The past couple of weeks have been a blur. Our adoption agency recommended we take some time on our own with the kids before having a lot of visitors or doing a lot of activities, so we have mostly been at home, taking care of kids and getting to know our daughter as she gets to know us and her new sister. The girls are so close in age and bonded almost instantly. The joy they find in each other's presence is heartwarming.

Tim and I look at each other as food flies off one of the highchairs. We have to laugh. It's a running joke that he is going back to work to rest. It feels good to be able to joke about something like that after what we've been through for the past four years since the stroke.

Laughter may really be the best medicine.

Giving Support
March 2012 – Four Years and Two Months After Stroke

It's quite the motley crew. Tim and I are sitting side by side in a confer-ence room at a hospital about a thirty-minute drive from our home. It's late afternoon during the week and we are happy to see all the familiar faces of those in this stroke support group that meets once a month. There are about twenty-five people sitting around a collection of six tables pushed together to form one large rectangular surface. In the room there are stroke survivors, their caregivers, and a speech language pathologist who facilitates the meeting. We exchange warm greetings and smiles with those around us. We belong here.

My mind drifts, and I am taken back to the memory of when we first started attending these meetings a few years ago. It was almost a year after Tim's stroke and, after months of encouragement by me and by Tim's own speech therapist, Tim finally agreed to go to one meeting, just one meeting. I was hoping one meeting would lead to more. I was back to work part-time, and Tim was spending a whole lot of his days alone. I knew in my gut that my husband needed to be around other people who had suffered strokes—especially those who were thriving, not just surviving. I knew I couldn't be his cheerleader in this particular arena. I knew there were things that I could never truly understand.

The first few meetings were uncomfortable for both of us, with me doing more talking than he did. He would sit back, listen, and observe. Then, over the few days after each meeting, we would spend hours dissecting it, reflecting on the stories we had heard. In the groups, we heard about struggles and wins both from the stroke survivors and from their caregivers. We listened to each other and to experts who were brought in to share their knowledge. We witnessed people who had bounced all the way back and witnessed those who had far more challenges than Tim. There were people with canes, people in wheelchairs, and people who couldn't speak many words at all. There were so many heartbreaking stories, as well as many of hope. There were stories of the impact of ableism, stories of being completely disregarded in public places, stories of being dismissed and disrespected by medical providers and insurance companies. There was anger and sadness and healing.

The people in the group ranged in age from twenty to eighty-five. There were couples and people who had weathered their strokes alone. There were some who had experienced one stroke and some who had survived multiple brain events. Many of them had aphasia. Tim's wasn't the worst case, and wasn't the best either. There were people from all walks of life, gathered to support each other and be supported in return. Given the diversity of the group, it was comforting to recognize that we all belonged.

The first couple of years Tim and I were on the receiving end of support, and then his role in the group started to change. The group celebrated his return to work, as well as our two adoptions. After that, we started being the ones to give. We welcomed new members, volunteered for tasks, brought treats, and participated more. We graduated from me driving Tim to the meetings, to him doing the driving with me as passenger, feeling a little like his driver's ed teacher and then, at times, to him driving to the meetings alone if we couldn't get a sitter.

I hear the door close to my left, the noise bringing me back to the present moment. I look around the room, seeing so many familiar faces, faces of people who have become like family. Today, the meeting starts off with Tim giving a mini-presentation on how technology helped him regain access to language more quickly and effectively. I watch him share, patiently answering questions about Dragon Speak, Natural Reader, and the use of audio books as ways to develop new neural pathways. It almost seems surreal to see him talking and sharing and offering to help others. He exudes both confidence and hope.

I lean back in my chair, smiling. Even though the past four years have been long and challenging, moments like this remind me of the power of community, the beauty of belonging, and the gift of walking down difficult roads in the presence of mentors and guides and friends. In this beloved support group, I have watched Tim move from getting support to giving it.

Today, I am thrilled to see my husband stepping back into his natural role as a leader.

California Road Trip
July 2012 – Four Years and Six Months After Stroke

pull off the freeway into yet another rest stop. Our daughters are crabby. Tim and I are crabby. We are on our way back to Oregon after visiting family in California and have been trapped in this car for way too many hours and it is taking its toll on all of us. We look at each other, clearly wondering what the hell we were thinking when we planned a road trip with our *two* two-year-old daughters. Today's six-hour drive has stretched to ten and the day's driving isn't over yet. Little kids and long car rides are not really a good match.

I open the car door just as dozens of seagulls start dive-bombing the car. It's the craziest thing. It's like something straight out of a *Twilight Zone* episode watched on a black and white TV. Hellish and surreal. I quickly close the door to assess my options. It appears these birds are used to being fed by people in cars and they are overly eager to get their next snack. Our daughters start screaming as if the birds are planning to eat *them*. The screaming sets my nerves even more on edge. I am tired. I have to pee, and I can't deal with the kids or the birds or any of it for even five more minutes. I am over it! I feel a rush of adrenalin and feel strangely empowered. I abruptly get out of the car, silently pleading with Tim to stay with the kids, and I walk-run to the restroom waving my arms like a lunatic, daring the damned birds to mess with me.

When I come out, the birds have moved on to another car. I smile, feeling oddly triumphant.

When I get back in the car, Tim is calmly giving the girls a snack and seems to be taking it all in stride.

I start laughing.

And so does he.

We can't stop laughing at the crazy dive-bombing birds and the absurdity of a flock of seagulls setting up shop at a rest stop so many miles away from the sea.

I silently take a snapshot of this moment in my mind, remembering how close we came to not having any of it. I feel waves of gratitude for the laughter, for our children, and for this marriage that has survived its own version of a road trip through hell.

Magic Tree House

September 2012 – Four Years and Eight Months After Stroke

Tim's voice is soothing. I am tucking one of our kids into bed and down the hall I can hear him reading a story to our other child. I recognize it as a *Magic Tree House* story. I'm not sure how much my daughter understands, as she is just starting to understand English, but his voice is slow and steady and very calming to her. I pause and listen for a few minutes, smiling at the sweetness of the bonding that is happening between the two of them. I have always admired his consistency and dedication and I can see how that will play out as our daughters get older. They will learn from him.

Tim is focusing on getting better at reading without the use of technology. He has excelled at using Dragon Speak software for writing and Natural Reader software for reading. The use of both of these tools has greatly improved his ability to read, write, and understand written language, but he is also committed to creating new neural pathways without the aid of assistance. His dedication to his recovery is unwavering.

He started by reading simple children's books but was quickly bored with them and their content. We discovered the *Magic Tree House* series of books and he began reading them on his own and to our daughters, a chapter or two at a time, enjoying the stories and feeling challenged by the language as well. Over time we purchased several dozen of these books and he read through them slowly at first and then more quickly as time went by.

There is something magical about how these fun little adventure stories brought healing magic into Tim's life and subsequently into the lives of our children.

Christmas Tree Joy
December 2012 – Four Years and Eleven Months After Stroke

The girls are two years old, the age when everything is exciting and every road is worth exploring. It's a cold mid-December day and our little family is bundled up in warm clothes and out among the trees at a Christmas tree farm. Tim and I talk and laugh as the girls run around, giggling and stomping in the mud in their cute little pink boots.

Things have settled down in the stroke recovery area. Tim is doing really well. He's back at work and is so happy to be once again excelling at the job he loves. At home we are deep in the weeds with parenting. It's both exhausting and wonderful.

Today we are searching for the perfect Christmas tree. The kids are ecstatic—not so much for the trees, more for the mud puddles. They radiate the pure delight that comes with being somewhere new and different and messy.

We drove about an hour from our home to get here. We walk around, select our favorite tree, and put a hat on it, as instructed, so someone can come and cut it down for us and haul it to our car. As we wander around in the trees, I find myself experiencing waves of gratitude for the blessings in my life.

Our daughters are happy and healthy.
Tim and I are happy and healthy.
Tim loves being back to work full-time.
We are continuing to figure out this parenting thing.
We are enjoying traveling once again.
We have friends and family who love and support us.
We are now a family of four.

Life is good.

I smile and breathe a huge sigh of relief as we put the tree on top of the van, pack up our muddy kids, and head home to start ringing in the holidays.

PART TWO

The Rogue Wave

"We insist on permanency, on duration, on continuity;
when the only continuity possible, in life as in love,
is in growth, in fluidity—in freedom, in the sense that
the dancers are free, barely touching as they pass,
but partners in the same pattern."

— Anne Morrow Lindbergh

Food Poisoning
December 2012 – Four Years and Eleven Months After Stroke

I feel like shit. My throat hurts, I can't take deep breaths, I'm achy, and I think I need to see a doctor. *Damn.* It's mid-afternoon on a weekday in December, colds are flying around, and I think I might have pneumonia. *Shit.* Tim is at work and I'm home with our two two-year-old daughters trying to figure out how I can logistically make this work. If Tim comes straight home or even leaves work a little early, I might be able to make it to urgent care before it closes. I am distracted from my thoughts by the sound of my phone ringing. It's Tim. He has good news. He received a large year-end bonus at work today. He's very excited. It's been such a long road back from the stroke that happened about five years ago. I wholeheartedly congratulate him and then ask him to please come home early so I can go see a doctor. He agrees to do so.

My phone rings again about an hour later and I'm surprised to see Tim's name pop up on the screen. I thought he'd be on his way home from work by now. He says he doesn't feel well. He says he's been throwing up, is really nauseous, and isn't sure he can drive. I'm alarmed. I jump into caregiver mode and ask about any other symptoms he might have. I also ask what he ate for lunch. I wonder if he has food poisoning. He says he feels weak from throwing up and may be dehydrated. He asks if I can come get him. What? Now all my alarm bells are really going off. I ask a lot of questions, trying to rule out a stroke, which is my biggest fear. It doesn't sound like he's having another stroke. He's speaking clearly and coherently. I relax. I hang up and call my mom who agrees to come over to stay with the girls. I am grateful she lives nearby.

I bundle up and start driving across town in rush-hour traffic to Tim's office, which is eighteen miles away. It's after 5:00 p.m. now. He calls again. He says he doesn't know if he can make it down to the lobby and everyone has left his floor and the building is always locked. I am now on high alert, really getting worried, and ask him to give me the number for his building security. I pull over and call security, relieved when someone answers the phone. I let the security guard know I'm on my way and ask him to please check on Tim. He agrees to do so. I am worried. I am still sick. I wonder if we can make it to urgent care in time or if we'll need to go to the ER. I wonder if they can see us both.

Forty-five minutes later, I finally pull up to the front of Tim's large office building. It's dark and the parking lot is empty. I am relieved to see the security guard waiting for me. He escorts me to Tim's office. We find Tim sitting in his chair at his desk. He looks pale and a little embarrassed by all the fuss but otherwise he seems normal. He says he still feels nauseous and isn't sure he can walk without throwing up. I gather up his belongings and the security guard helps me wheel Tim to the elevator in his office chair.

We take the elevator to the lobby and wheel Tim out to the car. He stands up and gets in on his own. I hand him a plastic bag—just in case he needs to throw up. We head back across town toward home. Traffic is still a total bitch, so I opt to stop at a hospital ER on the way, hoping we won't have to wait too long.

We arrive at the emergency entrance and I get a wheelchair for Tim and help him out of the car. I push him in out of the cold and leave to go park the car. When we approach the reception desk in the ER and check in, I describe Tim's symptoms and let them know he has a history of stroke. They don't seem too alarmed, so I am able to relax a little. They take his vitals and gather a bunch of information, and we settle in for a long wait in a lobby jam-packed with sick people. I feel right at home.

We sit for what feels like hours and Tim continues to quietly vomit into a bag provided by the nurse who took his vitals. When we finally get taken to a room in the ER, they give him something for nausea, which doesn't seem to help. He passes all the stroke-related tests—touch your nose, lift your arms, smile, etc. The nausea doesn't subside. We've been here for more than four hours at this point and they decide to have an on-call neurologist assess Tim via a video screen on a robot. The neurologist talks to him, asks him questions, and after just a few minutes asks him to stand up. Tim tries to stand up but can't hold his balance enough to stay upright. What the hell? I have to hold him to keep him from falling. The doctor looks alarmed and demands an MRI and bloodwork be done *now*!

With this, I start shaking and crying and have to sit down to keep from falling.

Tim is wheeled off to get an MRI and I know in my gut he doesn't have food poisoning; I *know* he is having another fucking stroke.

Waiting
December 2012 – Three Days After Second Stroke

I stare blankly at a clock on the wall in the large, L-shaped hospital waiting room, watching the seconds and minutes tick by. I shake my head and look around the empty room. There was a volunteer at a desk near the door when I came in, but that person must have left when my back was turned. I am fidgeting. I pull a book out of my bag to read then get distracted and put it away. I bring out my journal but can't focus, so I put that back in my bag as well. I move to a different chair, hoping I will be more comfortable. I sigh as I realize the discomfort is coming from inside me, not from something caused by the chair. I'm screwed. I am stuck in this room, alone with my thoughts.

Tim is in surgery. He's been in there for more than an hour. He is getting a filter put in his vena cava, the large vein that carries blood from the lower and middle body into the heart. They are doing this to prevent any large clots in his legs from moving up toward his heart or lungs. It's been a few days since his second stroke and evidently he still has many blood clots and there is some risk of another stroke. They are covering all the bases now. He's on blood thinners. He's in the ICU getting around-the-clock care, and today he's having a procedure to install a filter.

I can't sit still, so I get up to go to the restroom. The volunteer is back now, so I let them know where I'm going, indicating I will be right back. I go quickly, fearful I will miss the doctor when he comes out to give me an update after the surgery.

When I return to the waiting room, I sit back down in a different chair, wondering if looking out the window will help to calm me, but the gray skies and the view of concrete buildings outside make me feel worse, so I move again, this time to face the door I assume the doctor will come through. I write a note on my to-do list and stare at the clock, watching the second hand slowly click its way up the left side of the face.

I am crawling out of my skin. I take a few deep breaths, stand up and stretch, and move to yet another chair. I wish I had thought to ask a friend to join me here. I check the time on my phone to see if the clock on the wall is accurate. I try to remember exactly how long the doctor said the surgery would take. I can't remember. A family comes in and I welcome the distraction as the large group moves past me to a collection of couches and chairs near the window. They are laughing and talking, which annoys me. Now I am distracted by my irritation at their cheerfulness. I am starting to feel really anxious and wonder if anyone would notice if I started pacing. I decide against it and grab a magazine off the coffee table in front of me. I flip the pages absently, not able to read a single word. I look at the clock again and try to do the math. How much longer? Why is it taking so long?

I dig out my journal and start writing notes, hoping that writing my thoughts will bring some relief from the endless waiting. I scribble my feelings—my frustration to be going through *this* again. After almost five years, I finally had my husband back and now he's gone again. I'm scared about all the unknowns. Why is his body so full of blood clots? He was taking an aspirin each day as they prescribed. He was eating healthy, exercising, has no history of heart disease or high cholesterol. What are we missing? Why does he have blood clots? Another part of me is confident, knowing we can power through this like the last time, but my confidence ebbs as I ponder the blood clots, so many blood clots.

Another part of me knows I need to rest, but I have gotten good at ignoring that part. I have been on antibiotics for pneumonia for a few days now and I am constantly popping cough drops to keep the cough at bay. I am chugging coffee to stay awake and drinking tons of water to offset all the caffeine. I wonder if the caffeine is contributing to the anxiety I'm currently feeling. I ignore the thought and take a drink of my coffee. Another part of me is scared out of my mind. I am scared to death Tim will leave me alone with two young children. This stroke was not part of our plan.

I am still writing when the doctor says my name. I drop my journal and my pen and look up, checking his expression to see if I can read it. He's smiling, so I allow myself to take a deep breath. He sits down next to me and says the procedure went well and I feel tears of relief. I blink them back, no time for that. He tells me they will attempt to remove the filter in a few weeks and I nod. I'm afraid if I say anything, the tears will leak out and I will fall into a sobbing heap on the floor. I smile. He says I can see Tim soon. I nod again and pick up my journal and pen from the floor as he walks away. I jot a note about the surgery and pull out my phone to start making the obligatory phone calls to family and friends.

After making the calls, I notice the scared and anxious part of me slowly disappears into the background as the competent, albeit reluctant, caregiver steps forward.

The caregiver in me stands up, pastes on a smile, grabs her bag and her coffee, and walks down the hall to see her husband.

Holiday Love from Friends
December 2012 – One Week After Second Stroke

slowly walk through the door at home after a long day with Tim at the hospital and am greeted by a Christmas tree full of decorations and two very happy little girls. Our daughters are jumping up and down with joy and pulling me over to the magical tree. I am stunned and overwhelmed and feel tears of gratitude roll down my cheeks. I may be witnessing one of the kindest things anyone has ever done for me.

It's been about a week since Tim had his second stroke and he's still in the hospital, which is more than thirty minutes away from our home. The Christmas tree has been standing in our front room without decorations since we brought it home a couple of days before the stroke, a reminder of the desolation I feel each time I come home.

I am continuing to take antibiotics for pneumonia and still feel like I am slogging through cement everywhere I go. Taking care of our two-year-old daughters, dealing with Tim's work for his medical leave and short-term disability benefits, and worrying about our future has left me with absolutely nothing extra to devote to decorating, preparing, or shopping for Christmas.

Bah humbug.

While I was at the hospital today, an amazing friend and her kids came over and decorated our tree for us. They, along with my mom, have been taking turns watching the girls while I spend time at the hospital each day with Tim. He's still in the ICU so the kids have not been able to go with me to visit.

The girls pull me to the tree and start pointing at all their favorite ornaments. Their faces radiate pure joy. I feel so much love and gratitude in this moment. Many of the ornaments on the tree were gifts from my mom over more than twenty years of ornament exchanges, bringing back so many memories. Knowing I have friends who would do something like this for us and then having my daughters here to witness this kindness fills my heart with love.

I am learning that even though life can be shit at times, it can still be beautiful and touched with love.

The Angry Man
December 2012 – Two Weeks After Second Stroke

I take a slow, deep breath as I step into the elevator. I hesitate briefly before pressing the button for the fifth floor. I watch the lights change as the elevator passes from floor to floor, feeling my discomfort increase as I travel upward. I exit on the fifth floor, turn left, and walk through one of the large metal doors into the inpatient rehabilitation wing of the hospital. I am shaking. It's been two weeks since Tim's second stroke and he has been transferred to this hospital for rehab. He's mainly here to learn to walk again, as the stroke severely impacted his balance. What had been hope has now turned to fear. This stroke feels so different from the first one. He seems so different. He's not himself. I'm not sure how to feel.

I slowly wander down the hall looking left and right for the correct room number. This is my first time here and I feel strangely out of place. I inexplicably fear the nurses will ask me to leave, so I pick up my pace and walk quietly and quickly down the hall, passing the nurses' station, and stopping when I locate my husband's room on the left.

I cautiously open the door and see Tim sitting up in a large hospital bed. The room is eerily quiet, but he is not asleep. He is wide awake and looks a little agitated. I have brought him a framed photograph of our family and I set it on the table that is positioned over his bed. I smile at him as I show him the photo of us with our daughters. The photo was taken a couple of weeks before the stroke. Today is Christmas Eve, and I am hoping a family holiday photo will bring him a little joy. We are postponing our Christmas celebration until he comes home. I say hello and launch into small talk about the kids and our day and how happy I am that he is now only five minutes away from our home. The previous hospital was often at least a thirty-minute drive. He was there for the past two weeks, with most of it spent in the ICU.

Tim looks at me and scowls. I ask what is going on and he slowly lets me know that they have scheduled him for speech therapy. Internally I am thinking speech therapy will be great, but I am confused by his statement. I tell him I am confused. I ask if he doesn't like the speech therapist. He's still glaring at me, and I suddenly feel nauseous. I don't know what to say. He eventually says he doesn't *need* speech therapy. He says he already fixed his aphasia. His words are angry, and he spits them at me.

His aphasia is definitely worse than it was a few weeks ago, before the second stroke, and I wonder if he is worried he will have to start all over. I let him know that the doctors say this regression often happens with aphasia after a subsequent stroke and I share that they also believe he will recover his speech deficits quickly. He shakes his head and angrily repeats that he doesn't *need* speech therapy. He is still glaring at me. He points his finger at me and says I'm wrong and they're wrong and he won't do speech therapy. The venom in his voice stills me. This angry defiance is unexpected, and I don't know what to say. I stand by his bed, staring at him, feeling the tears fill my eyes. I blink them back and move toward the door, letting him know I need to get back home to the kids.

I don't say good-bye. I find my way back to the elevator, step in, and take a breath as it descends to the main floor. I hold my composure until I reach my car in the parking garage. I close the car door, lay my head on the steering wheel, and allow the tears to flow.

What the hell happened to my husband?

Who is this angry person pretending to be him?

Recovering vs. Transforming
January 2013 – One Month After Second Stroke

I roll my eyes and sigh. I am sitting in Tim's hospital room in an inpatient rehabilitation wing of the hospital near our home. Tim completed a couple of weeks in the first hospital and has been at this facility for a couple more. We are listening to one of Tim's doctors ramble on about recovery and what to expect after discharge. Tim continues to be angry and frustrated with his situation—understandably so—and I am exhausted, both physically and emotionally. I hear the doctor saying something, but honestly it sounds like Charlie Brown's teacher is talking. I tune him out.

Something inside of me shifts. I realize that the "recovery" Tim has been working his ass off to achieve doesn't exist. The "recovery" I have been hoping and praying for is simply a pipedream. Tim will get better and he will heal, but he will never go back to being the same person he was before.

The doctor is still talking, and I want to scream at him (and the world) that "recovery" from brain injuries is simply not possible. It's a brick wall at the end of the road. We have both spent the past five years focusing on Tim's "recovery" and trying to get back to our lives as they were before. We keep being disappointed over and over and over again. Even though his brain is healing and new neural pathways are being created, they are not the old pathways. Those pathways no longer exist. There is no going back.

According to Dictionary.com, the meaning for the word *recover* (a verb) means the following: "to get back or regain (something lost or taken away); to regain the strength, composure, balance, or the like, of (oneself); to regain health after being sick, wounded, or the like (often followed by *from*); to regain a former and better state or condition." Tim will not get back what he lost. What grows anew in his brain will be wonderful but different.

I look up at the doctor and realize, for the first time, that he is selling the wrong thing. He is preaching "recovery" when transformation is all that is truly available.

We need to begin the process of transformation.

Christmas in January
January 2013 – One Month After Second Stroke

We are pretending it's Christmas Day. It's a random day in late January and I stayed up super late last night wrapping gifts and putting together toys for a magical "Christmas" morning for our daughters. After his recent stints in the hospital and rehab center, Tim is primarily dealing with balance issues and learning to walk without a walker. Fortunately, our kids are too young to care about the calendar.

Since this is the first Christmas our second daughter has been with our family, we decided to wait and celebrate when Tim got home. Basically that gave me an extra month to overspend on gifts, buying way too many presents in an attempt to make up for the giant curveball that was thrown at our family. Even as I purchased the gifts, I knew it wouldn't really matter. The girls are two years of age. They would be happy with one fabulous toy and a piece of candy. I, on the other hand, was trying to fill up a very dark and empty hole inside of me.

This morning the girls are delighted with their presents, the music, and the Christmas lights. Their smiles and laughter bring comfort on this dreary day. Tim and I tiptoe around each other. His frustration and anger radiate off him and I try to stay out of his energetic orbit. We are both pretty freaked out about the second stroke and the upheaval it has caused in our lives. We are both trying to cope in whatever way we can. This time I know how hard it's going to be. Tim takes his frustration and turns inward. I take mine and turn to shopping for the kids.

Unfortunately, we can't ignore or buy our way out of the shit that happens in life.

Merry freaking Christmas.

Shots to the Gut
February 2013 – Two Months After Second Stroke

Tim lifts his shirt and waits patiently as I give him another shot in the stomach. He grimaces but doesn't flinch or move. Because I have given many shots to our cats over the years for diabetes and pain control, giving shots is not a big deal. This "nursing" care does seem to shift things though. Since the second stroke, the relationship between my husband and me just keeps getting weirder. I am the caregiver and he is the one receiving care. It's hard to ignore this dynamic when some aspect of it is in my face every single day. I wonder if we can even be considered spouses anymore.

Because the medical professionals are unable to figure out exactly why Tim had a second stroke (or why he had the first stroke, for that matter) or why his body is full of blood clots, they are doing a bunch of tests and procedures, in addition to taking lots of preventative measures to ensure another stroke doesn't happen. In addition to having two very young daughters, I am now tasked with managing my husband's care with multiple providers, his medical leave from work, and all the insurance nonsense, all while trying to manage my own emotions around what is happening.

It's a lot.

It's a whole lot to manage.

Tim still has the filter in his vena cava artery, surgically placed to help prevent blood clots from moving up toward his heart or lungs. He also met with a cardiologist and will likely be getting an AMPLATZER device placed in his otherwise healthy heart to seal the small hole he's had since birth—the hole that allowed two large blood clots to pass through to his brain. They are doing a bunch of tests to rule out cancer as well, because, apparently, cancer can also cause blood clots. Every hypothesis feels like a punch to the gut. It's bad enough he's had two strokes. Now I get to worry about more blood clots, a heart procedure, and possibly cancer.

Right now Tim is prepping for a colonoscopy and is being given a different blood thinner that will hopefully make the procedure more safe. The doctor explained that it's necessary so Tim doesn't bleed out if they have to do a biopsy. (Good God! Yet another punch to the gut.) The blood thinner he needs is not available in pill form. Hence the shots in the stomach.

I dispose of the needle and sit down. I try to take some deep breaths and pull myself together. One of the most challenging things about being my husband's caregiver is the inability to create any distance between us. I don't get to go home after a "shift" and get a hug from my person. We are both taking hits to the gut and neither one of us has any emotional energy left to support or console the other. My caregiver role has become my only role with my husband and it's pretty clear that even though it's necessary, we both fucking hate it.

The Bruise
April 2013 – Four Months After Second Stroke

It's mid-afternoon on a Sunday in the springtime and I am sitting in our living room reading a story to our daughters, who are fascinated with books at the moment. It's been a few months since the second stroke and Tim is recovering from a procedure in which a device called an AMPLATZER was implanted in his heart. That happened three days ago, and he is home and seems to be back to his normal, post-stroke self.

It was one of those *wonders of modern medicine* moments. The cardiologist used a needle to go in through the femoral artery and was able to implant a device to close the small hole in Tim's heart that had been there since birth. The hole was not the problem—one in five people have a hole in the heart. The fact that the hole was allowing blood clots to travel to his brain *was* a problem. After two large strokes, it was deemed necessary to close the hole, despite the good health of his heart. It is believed that Tim's blood clots are caused by a rare, unnamed blood-clotting disorder. The device was implanted to reduce the chance of any future strokes. The procedure was a success and Tim came home after only one night in the hospital. We all slept better that night.

I look up as Tim comes out to the living room. He has just taken a shower and asks if I can take a look at his bruise at the site where they entered the femoral artery to place the device in his heart. He thinks the bruise might be a little too big. I remember the discharge instructions which clearly stated to watch for bruising and if a bruise gets bigger than a quarter, we should contact the hospital immediately. I get up and nonchalantly walk to the master bathroom, leaving the girls to continue "reading" on their own. I recoil when I see the bruise! It's not the size of a quarter. It's the size of a football. Holy shit! I take a deep breath and run to find the discharge paperwork and call the hospital. I am shaking. They instruct me to get him to the ER as fast as possible or call an ambulance.

Breathe. Breathe. Breathe.

I call my neighbor. She's home and willing to come watch our daughters until my mom can come over. *Thank God.* Tim and I are in the car within five minutes and on our way to the hospital across town. I call my mom on the way, asking if she can relieve my neighbor, not knowing how long we will be gone. By some twist of luck, people were home and able to step in and help. We didn't need to call an ambulance. We don't say much on the way to the hospital, both of us lost in our own thoughts about what this means and what will need to happen to stop the internal bleeding that is clearly happening. We are now praying that modern medicine can fix this latest setback, wondering if we will ever be able to fully let down our guard and rest.

Pseudoaneurysm
April 2013 – Four Months After Second Stroke

I may have broken a few traffic laws on the way to the hospital. I honestly don't remember. Tim and I are at the ER after being instructed to *go immediately or call 911*. I had called the hospital and shared about the bruising in Tim's groin area and the alarm of the nurse raised my alarm and here we are. Tim's heart is fine. Evidently, the femoral artery is not.

Tim is experiencing what is known as a *pseudoaneurysm*, a swelling of the wall of the artery. Thankfully, we made it to the hospital in time and the wall of the artery did not burst. The swelling is close to where they went in with a small tube to implant the device in his heart three days ago. A pseudoaneurysm occurs when a blood vessel wall is injured and the leaking blood collects in the surrounding tissue. Now that they have diagnosed the problem, the doctor explains the next steps. They will start with compression. If that doesn't work, they will go in with a needle and do some sort of patch on the artery wall. As with most medical procedures, I nod and assume they know what they are doing.

I stand by as several medical practitioners come into the room with an ultrasound machine. I'm confused. I'm no longer sure who's in charge. A man in scrubs (who may or may not be a doctor) describes that he will be locating the pseudoaneurysm on the ultrasound and then applying compression to the area for five minutes to see if they can get the bleeding to stop. I am skeptical. *Why aren't they wheeling him into emergency surgery?* The man in scrubs takes the ultrasound wand and pushes on the area on Tim's upper leg and when he finds the spot on the ultrasound, he lifts his own knee (yes, his own knee) and kneels on that spot on Tim's upper leg, applying compression. Tim winces and closes his eyes, clearly in pain. I am horrified. Time crawls by as I stand frozen. *Should I say something? Should I demand they give him painkillers or anesthesia? What should I do?* I wince and say nothing.

After five very long minutes, the man takes his knee off Tim's groin and checks the area again with the ultrasound. It didn't work. Shit. The man in scrubs says he will try again. I look at Tim. He looks as horrified as I feel but tells the practitioner to go ahead. As the man kneels again on Tim's groin area to apply compression, I can feel myself getting nauseous. Tim has his eyes closed tightly and his whole face shows that he is in pain. I am shocked. *How are they actually doing this? How can they be using sheer force to stop this bleed? We are in one of the top hospitals in a large city. This is not happening on the side of the road after a car crash.*

Another minute ticks by and I can't take it anymore. I yell, "Enough! Stop! He's in pain. This is not okay." The man takes his knee off Tim's groin and I feel myself take a breath, but I can't stop my shaking. He checks the artery again using the ultrasound. It didn't work.

They inform me that Tim will now need a procedure to repair the artery and will need to be under anesthesia when they do it. Tim looks relieved, completely wiped out, and like he may throw up. I hope he doesn't throw up. The medical workers all shuffle out of the room, taking their ultrasound machine with them. I send them daggers with my eyes as they go.

I sit down in a chair next to the bed, still shaking with a mix of anger and helplessness. I ask Tim how he's doing. He's too exhausted to talk. I am thankful he will be asleep during the procedure and won't remember it.

As he drifts off to sleep, I think about all the close calls Tim has experienced over the past five years and, even though I am mad as hell at all doctors right now, deep down I am so damned grateful that, once again, they are here to save my husband's life.

*The cardiologist was able to repair the artery and Tim recov-
ered and returned home after three days in the hospital. The
football-sized bruise took many weeks to fully fade away. It still
boggles my mind that the heart procedure itself resulted in a
very brief hospital stay and a complication at the injection site
resulted in a potentially life-threatening emergency.*

The Demise of the Sin Dawg
April 2013 – Four Months After Second Stroke

I need to run to the grocery store to get a few things. It's mid-afternoon on a Saturday and it's been a busy day. Shopping is the last thing on my to-do list before I allow myself to sit down with a cup of tea and a treat. I imagine a peaceful drive to the store, a quiet stroll up and down the aisles, and coming home in a state of Zen, perfect for my little tea party for one. I laugh as I'm pretty sure my imagination is a little unrealistic.

Our daughters are two years old. Tim is still recovering from his second large stroke and the procedure to close the hole in his heart. I wonder if I can leave the girls home with him. I haven't left them home with their dad since he was released from the hospital. I imagine them playing quietly as he sits nearby. Maybe? I know a "quick" trip to the grocery store can take an hour or more if I have to pack up the kids and take them with me. I'm torn but seriously considering giving it a try.

I check in with Tim to see if he feels up to watching the girls for about thirty minutes. He says yes. I ask him again, just to make sure. He says he's sure. I am delighted for the chance to go quickly without our daughters. Tim is watching sports on TV and seems kind of sleepy, so I remind him as I leave that he needs to *watch* the kids. He agrees several times and off I go.

I am grateful for the chance to go alone and to shop without inter-ruption, but the peaceful experience I imagined is hijacked by the constant worry about Tim and the girls. It's like a radio station that is always on—sometimes turned up high and sometimes turned so low it barely registers—but it is always on and always pulls at least some of my attention. I sigh as I push the grocery cart to a checkout lane.

Less than thirty minutes later, I am home. I get out of the car and automatically open the sliding rear door on the van. I catch myself, remembering the girls aren't in the car, and push the button to close the door. I pick up my groceries from the passenger seat and head for the front door. I walk in the door and find Tim asleep on the couch.

(*Uh oh.*)

The house is eerily quiet.

(*Uh oh again.*)

Panic explodes inside my body, my heart starts pounding, and I feel wild-eyed and a little crazy. I stuff it all down and yell at Tim. "Wake up! Where are the girls?" I drop the grocery bags on the dining room table as I run to the kitchen.

What I see is unbelievable. It looks like my kitchen threw up on itself. Both girls are there, and I breathe a grateful prayer. One of our daughters looks like she has bathed herself in my Sin Dawg. (In case you are not aware, a Sin Dawg is a yummy cinnamon-sugar bread roll made by Dave's Killer Bread. It's also the treat I was looking forward to having with my tea.) The brown cinnamon-sugar sticky goo is all over her face and her favorite yellow shirt. It is also on her hands and on her arms up to her elbows. She proudly informs me it is also in her tummy. It is smeared on the floor in front of the refrigerator and, to my surprise, it is also on the wall in the hallway that leads to the bathroom.

The girls somehow managed to pull the metal fruit basket, full of fruit, off the butcher block island and had peeled one banana, which is laying squished on the floor along with all the other fruit. (They did put the empty banana peel back up on the counter, which was really nice of them.) Our other daughter's shirtsleeves are wet up to her elbows, which perplexes me until I realize that the cat's water bowl is upside down and there is water on the floor in the breakfast nook. I scan the room and notice the girls also managed to bypass a magnet lock and open a kitchen cabinet and the contents of the cabinet are scattered across the floor.

At this point, I'm not sure if I should laugh or cry or maybe explode with anger at their dad. Surprisingly, my next thought is *How could they ruin my Sin Dawg? I wanted to eat that!*

I take a few deep breaths, strip off the girls' messy clothes, and send them out to their dad in the living room so I can start to clean up. At this point one of our daughters takes off her diaper and starts running around yelling, "Poop, poop." I almost fall on the floor laughing. My husband most definitely owes me a Sin Dawg!

Now, upon reflection, I still see that experience as a sweet memory that makes me smile. It was a mess that day but, thankfully, not a tragedy. I also see how something shifted inside of me that day. I realized how alone I was in caring for our daughters. I realized how dramatically Tim's two strokes had affected him and how those injuries left him unable to care for our daughters on his own. I had been so focused on his recovery and my hope for the future that I wasn't living in reality.

I realized that my primary role was caregiver to my husband and kids. I reluctantly accepted that role, watching as the light in my life dimmed a little more.

Setting the Intention
June 2013 – Six Months After Second Stroke

Floor-to-ceiling windows bathe the space in natural light. I close my eyes and feel the warmth of the sun on my face. I am sitting with my life coach in her office, a small room on the fifth floor of a large concrete building. It's been about six months since Tim's second stroke and even though things are tense and challenging at home, I'm feeling called to start thinking about returning to work in a couple of years. This was our plan. I was going to stay home with the girls until they started school and then I would return to my work as a psychotherapist. As a caregiver to my husband and to my two young daughters, I am no longer sure I want to return to a profession that involves caregiving. Doing caregiving 24/7 is a little too much. My body is clearly saying no, as evidenced by the panic I experience each time I consider it. I am here in coaching to explore my options, knowing I will need to someday go back to working outside the home.

My coach and I are exploring ideas, namely the idea of launching my writing—my voice—out into the world. As I consider sharing myself in this vulnerable way, I feel my throat tighten and my hands begin to sweat. My stomach churns and I shift slightly in my chair, trying to relax so I can alleviate the discomfort inside and focus on the discussion. The fear of criticism has kept my voice hidden for *decades*. The irony of becoming the voice of my husband is not lost on me. As I became his voice, my voice was pushed even further into hiding. The agony of going through the motions without making my presence known has taken its toll. The need for change has brought me here to this magical office full of light.

I take a deep breath and lean into the light.

I am determined to finally take some sort of action toward releasing my voice into the world. The plan that emerged last week was to take one small step toward addressing a barrier that's in the way. For me, the biggest barrier has always been the fear of criticism of my writing, which has been alive in my thoughts since high school. I don't share my stories or poetry with anyone.

Today I make the bold decision to write a poem to my critics (both internal and external) and see what happens. I know on some deep level it's finally time.

I feel the words first in my hands. A gentle rocking back and forth, as if pouring sand from one hand to the other. As the motion continues, this poem to my past and future critics comes pouring out of me.

My Song

I hold your voice
in the palm of my hand
heavy, loud, condescending.
I take a breath
and slowly
roll the words
from one hand to the other
encouraging the disappointment and judgment
to fall away
quietly through my fingers
like grains of sand.
And with the sand
the fear subsides
and I am left holding
my song.

This poem truly marks the beginning of my journey to reclaiming my voice.

In this moment, in this sunlit room, I courageously set the intention to write and share my caregiver story, so that I can begin to breathe more light and hope into a very dark time for myself and maybe even for others as well.

Five years after writing that poem, in a bizarre twist of circumstances, I jumped at the chance to write my very first song. Writing a song wasn't on my bucket list and it wasn't something I had always wanted to do, and yet the idea of doing it ignited something in me and I decided to take a leap of faith. I dove in and wrote a song. I knew I wanted to include spoken-word poetry in the song but struggled to find words that resonated. After months of writing and creating, I finished the song, deciding it was simply good enough.

I had completely forgotten about the poem referenced above—particularly the ending in which "I am left holding my song." Back when I wrote the poem, "my song" was a metaphor. This poem came back into my consciousness on my flight to LA to record my song. It was a magical gift. It worked. The poem now lives in my song. The song is called "Pictures" and was released on all the major platforms in 2020. It was the first time my writing had ever been released in such a public way. It substantially reduced my fear of sharing my writing. Listening to the song grounds me when I step out and do scary things, especially things for which I fear I will be criticized. From that grounded space I was finally able to put energy into writing this caregiver story.

Our Crazy Communication Dance
June 2013 – Six Months After Second Stroke

I sit here in my office staring out the window into our beautiful back-yard, looking at the lovely curved retaining wall that Tim and I built. We constructed it a few years after buying this house. It was the first big house project we did together. We didn't hire someone to do it; we wanted to do it ourselves. We had a vision and we put a shit-ton of effort into creating that vision. I smile at the memory. I also remember some of the arguments we had during the weeks of building the damned thing and how, ultimately, we each had to let go of a little bit of control. I chuckle quietly at that memory. We eventually found our rhythm and the wall turned out to be amazing. I am proud of our accomplishment and how we were able to laugh at those construction squabbles.

I shake my head and look back down at my computer and read through my journal entry from yesterday.

Tim does this thing that makes me crazy. He will say something odd and I will question it and then he will deny he said it and then we fight and then I get angry for communicating and we argue and argue and then he gets over it and apologizes and I am left feeling frustrated and a little bit more distant from him in my heart. I hate this dance. He owns that I am the only person he talks to that way and I hate that.
Why do we have to be so mean to those we love?
Why does it work that way?

Aphasia is a horrible condition. I know it affects his ego when I challenge him or correct him but I honestly just want to help or am genuinely confused by his words and then he launches into this complete denial of saying what he said. It makes me crazy and I so often just want out when it happens. What I really want is for him to come back and be the way he was.

As I read through this journal entry and others, I am surprised by how often I use the phrase *makes me crazy*. I wonder if I am going a little crazy. Then I look out in the yard and see the wall and remember how we used to communicate. Like all couples, we had our disagreements and arguments, but they never felt crazy-making. He never used to deny saying something. He would own his viewpoint, even if we disagreed. If I was confused by something he said, he would say it in another way. He wouldn't get mad. The arguments of the past never made me want to leave.

As I reread that last sentence in my journal entry, *What I really want is for him to come back and be the way he was,* I feel the doubt creep in. I wonder if it's the doubt that is keeping me up at night. I tell myself over and over and over that he will recover, but I wonder if, deep down inside my gut, I am just not sure.

What if he's not able to come back and be the way he was? What then?

Will we just keep doing this crazy communication dance until I leave?

Broken Memories
June 2013 – Six Months After Second Stroke

This fancy restaurant with white tablecloths feels quite luxurious after eating most of our meals for the past six months at home with two toddlers. It's midday on a weekend and Tim and I are seated at a round table in a beautiful old downtown space with my cousin, his wife, and a couple of friends we are just getting to know. We are here to have lunch before going to see a play. Tim and I haven't had many social outings since the second stroke. I am excited to have this time away from the kids, to be out with adults, and to be able to step away from the daily acts of caregiving.

As we all catch up on each other's lives, I share about our daughters and how life is going with two little ones at home. Someone asks Tim how he is liking being a dad to two daughters. He tells everyone that he never wanted kids. I am stunned. I look at him like he has two heads and the extra one is talking. *What the fuck?* I am too stunned to even say anything.

I flash back to the early years of our relationship when we were discussing marriage and kids and how we wanted our lives to look. Neither one of us was itching to have kids right away and we agreed to wait and adopt if and when we were ready. His rationale was pragmatic—too many kids already on the planet—mine was born out of a deep desire to adopt from an orphanage. Neither one of us was ready to be a parent at that time. We tabled it and moved on with our lives.

My thoughts then flash to a conversation in 2006, many years before this lunch. The two of us were sitting in our favorite restaurant having a late dinner. We were seated at the bar in a fabulous bistro, eating and talking. It was dark and stormy outside, giving the restaurant a cozy glow. Our conversation was meandering around from tropical vacations to friends to our upcoming plans for the holiday season. On that day I knew deep in my soul that I was meant to raise a child. We had a serious conversation about it and agreed to table the idea until he had a chance to give it some serious thought.

My thoughts then flash forward a few more months and I recall a time in our car, driving along the Oregon Coast on a bright and chilly day. Tim was driving and I was staring out the window at the beautiful view. We were at the beach for a long weekend with some of our closest friends and we were out by ourselves to check out a pottery studio and do a little sightseeing. Tim was staring out the windshield and nonchalantly said to me that he wanted to be a dad, he wanted to raise a child, and thought we should move forward with adopting. My mouth dropped open. I was speechless. We were both so incredibly happy. I can't remember a day when we were so happy together.

I smile. I hear someone asking me a question and I am right back having lunch in the restaurant with Tim, my cousins, and some friends. I feel the awkwardness that is present at the table. I make a joke out of what Tim just said, blame the aphasia, and move the conversation forward, wondering how the hell this can be happening. I know I'm not crazy. I know his happiness and excitement were real. I sit there in a funk—so damned angry at the strokes that robbed me of my husband; the strokes that, in many ways, also robbed our children of the father they could have had.

Years later, Tim and I had a conversation about that day in the restaurant. He said he had no memory of ever saying such a thing about having children. I was somewhat relieved to hear that. That string of events was a window into how tangled some of his thoughts, statements, and memories became following his brain injuries. Life with aphasia impacts everything—past, present, and future, and can sometimes taint even the most treasured memories.

Stuffing the Grief
June 2013 – Six Months After Second Stroke

It's really late and I am too wired to sleep. I read over the journal entry I just wrote and try to glean some wisdom from it, hoping to know what to do.

I am really struggling with Tim's aphasia right now. He has chosen to define himself by his strokes and the aphasia and it drives me crazy. He is so much more than that but chooses to spend most of his free time talking about the stroke and the aphasia and surfing the web about them. I just want to hear an original thought or idea come from him. We used to have really interesting conversations and I die a little inside each day as a result of this. I have lost my best friend and I want him back. I want him to be excited about my interests and I want to be excited about his. I feel like I have lived and breathed enough stroke-related information for a while and just want a hiatus from it. (So why the hell am I planning to write a book about it?) Seriously, I want to take something awful and create something beautiful and helpful. I just don't want to live and breathe it all day every day. I want my husband back.

As I read these words, I am painfully aware of how stroke-centric our lives have become and how painful it is for me to live in this bubble. I can't get any distance at all from the cause of my grief, so it's not surprising that I am not able to fully experience it so I can heal. I have gotten really good at ignoring the pain, stuffing it away, and pretending all is well. As I read my own words, I feel the tears start to fill my eyes. I can't hide from myself. I will the tears to stop, feeling the irritation in my throat as I choke them back. I don't want to feel sad. I don't want to feel the grief. I honestly don't want to feel anything right now.

I don't want to be living and breathing this trauma all day every day. I just want things to go back to the way they were, to the days when our lives centered around love.

When Helpers Aren't Helpful
June 2013 – Six Months After Second Stroke

I'm sitting across from a psychotherapist, feeling small and unheard, and she looks like she is falling asleep. *What the hell?* I'm sitting in a comfortable office in a beautiful neighborhood, attempting to spill my deepest thoughts and challenges to this drowsy woman. Granted, it's late afternoon and my story is a long and winding one, but really? Falling asleep? This is the latest in a long list of grievances I have with this terrible therapist and more evidence of how I don't stand up for myself and set boundaries.

It's been about six months since Tim's second stroke, and I am really struggling. I continue to ramble on, sharing my woes, and she continues to try to keep herself awake. She seems more fascinated by Tim's story than mine and spends a fair amount of time trying to assess his mental health, which I find weird and not very supportive. I find this all the more disturbing as I have been a licensed counselor/psycho-therapist for a number of years. I know she is doing a terrible job and I still can't seem to say anything to her. The power differential is alive and well inside of me and in our relationship. I wonder why I can advocate so well for Tim and be so shitty at doing so for myself.

I continue to talk about my feelings and realize that these sessions have been the only time in the years since Tim's first stroke when I have been able to talk about my feelings openly and freely. *That,* I decide, is worth the money I am spending on these sessions with this terrible therapist. She wakes up enough to make the comment, "Well, it's not like you can just go to the ocean and scream about this." I look at her curiously and say, "Why not?" Why couldn't I do that? I feel a seed of hope start to blossom inside of me. I need a break. I need a couple of days alone, away from my kids, my husband, and the drudgery that has become my life.

For the first time since coming to see her, I feel a tiny bit better. It's not lost on me that I only feel better because I am ignoring her advice and choosing to do the opposite, but I still feel a tiny bit better. For today, that is enough.

I took my weekend away and found it very helpful. I scribbled and screamed my feelings onto the page in poem after poem after poem and found healing in the wake of it. I am grateful to her for shaking something loose that day, however inadvertently.

I did finally fire that person as my therapist when she made an off-hand inappropriate comment about my brother. It was over the line. I ended the relationship, wondering how the Universe could have paired me with that person, wondering if it was somehow intentional to help me find my voice.

Getting Schooled
July 2013 – Seven Months After Second Stroke

I park the car outside a small office building a few miles away from our home. It's mid-afternoon and the kids and I are picking up Tim from his first psychotherapy appointment. He finally agreed to see someone for his anxiety and depression. I've been wanting him to get therapy for years and even more so since his second stroke and I am hopeful it went well. This therapist was recommended by one of his doctors. He gets in the car and doesn't say much. I start driving home and cautiously ask him how it went. He says it went okay and says he made an appointment to go back the following week. I breathe a sigh of relief. Maybe the therapist can help the old Tim come back.

During dinner, Tim mentions the appointment and starts talking about PTSD and what he learned in his appointment. I listen as he explains how he has been traumatized by his strokes. I agree with him and tell him so. As he continues to talk, he takes on the role of the expert and starts pontificating. I feel rage bubbling up inside of me. I feel hot and a little disoriented. I feel so fucking invisible. I want to scream in his face that I am right here and my words matter too. I have been sharing this information with him for years. I wonder if he even remembers that I went to graduate school and have a degree in counseling psychology. I wonder if he remembers that I am trained and licensed to diagnose people with mental health disorders, including PTSD. Does he think I have been talking out of my ass when I tell him I am worried about him? I stare at him incredulously, wondering if some-one's head can actually explode. I tell him, through gritted teeth, that I am well aware of PTSD and how it shows up and why. He dismisses me and continues to school me with his learning from his one appointment. I ignore him. I stand up and take my uneaten plate of food to the kitchen and toss it into the sink.

I grab my purse and keys and tell him I need to go to the store. I ask him to watch the kids for a little while. I don't look at him or the kids. I leave without even saying goodbye.

In this moment, as I walk out the front door, I have no idea where I will go.

In this moment, as I walk out the front door, I am not absolutely certain I will ever come back.

Attraction

July 2013 – Seven Months After Second Stroke

It's getting late, but the sun is still casting a warm orange glow through the windows of our living room. It's a mid-summer evening. The girls are in bed and the house is blissfully quiet. Tim and I are sitting in this home that we both love. He sits in a chair. I'm on the comfy sofa across from him. I am reading a book and enjoying the silence after a very noisy day with two three-year-olds. I look up and see Tim staring at me, not talking, just staring.

I ask him what's on his mind. He continues to stare and then says, calmly and without any venom, that he is no longer attracted to me. I feel the verbal knife as it pierces my stomach and then moves up and slowly cuts out my heart. He says he isn't trying to hurt me; he's just being honest. He says he doesn't feel attraction to anyone since his second stroke. He doesn't seem distressed. He says it's not personal and yet I still feel the pain of his words. "No longer attracted to you" feels pretty personal. I don't know how to process this information.

I sit here wondering what we are, what we have become. Are we husband and wife, disabled person and caregiver, household business partners, co-parents, just friends? I feel my walls slowly go up, that familiar protective glaze coating my outside to protect my inside. I don't know what to say. What do you say to something like that? I simply say, "Okay," as my soul screams, *Not okay*.

Bit by bit, I am coming to understand that things are different, we are different, our relationship is different. I have no idea what tomorrow will bring. I have no idea if we will ever fall in love again, with each other or with other people.

I wonder if I am willing to give up being loved.

Halt
August 2013 – Nine Months After Second Stroke

It's a weekday, late in the summer in the middle of the night. Tim is asleep. The kids are asleep—one in the middle of our bed and one in a toddler bed across the room. I can't sleep. Again. *Damn it.* I listen to all the gentle breathing of the people around me and instead of feeling lulled into slumber, Tim's ability to sleep so peacefully in the midst of our crazy life just pisses me off. I get up, go downstairs to the office, flip on the light, sit down at my desk, and open the journal on my laptop. I start furiously typing, trying to make some sense out of my life, my feelings, my insomnia.

From the outside looking in, I am functioning reasonably well. The girls are enrolled in a cooperative preschool and will be starting soon. I will be volunteering there as well. This will be their first school experience and they are so excited. I am maintaining contact with family and friends and doing my best to deal with the latest stroke bomb that was thrown our way about nine months ago. Tim is back at work, and I am doing my best to hold it all together. On the outside.

On the inside, I am a writhing mass of grief and rage.

I type the following words in my journal:

Still freaking mad all the time and know I need to get some decent therapy to deal with some of the grief and confusion that I am feeling. So very conflicted all of the time. Reflecting today on the HALT acronym. Hungry? Yes, all the time. Angry? Yes, all the time. Lonely? Yes, all the time. Tired? Yes, all the time.

I read the words again and thank God I don't drink. That would certainly add another layer of fresh hell to this mess. I do wonder how long I can keep eating garbage food before it takes a toll on my health. I wonder when the venom of my rage will come flying out of me and land all over the people I love. I wonder if it's possible to die a slow death from loneliness even when surrounded by people every goddamned day. I wonder how long I can continue getting three or four hours of sleep a night before that takes a toll as well.

I think the point of the HALT acronym is to help someone stop and ask some questions before doing something self-destructive. I keep typing.

What do I do when there is never enough food to make my hunger go away?

What do I do if the feelings of anger get sparked on a daily basis?

What do I do if connections with friends and family don't stop the loneliness I feel in my marriage?

What do I do if I'm bone tired and still can't sleep?

I close my laptop and stare out the window into the dimly lit back-yard, wondering what really needs to halt and wondering what the fallout will be when it all finally does comes to a stop.

Storming Out

December 2013 – One Year After Second Stroke

The kids are cranky. They're done eating and are now fussing with their plates and silverware. It's almost 8 p.m., dinner is on the table, and Tim still isn't home from work. It's already dark outside and I am totally exhausted. The girls finished eating a while ago, but I know if I start to clean up I will be committed to that task for the next hour. I push the food around on my plate, watching out the window for the lights of Tim's car.

It's been about a year since Tim's second stroke, and he is back working full-time. He had been working from home, but concentrating with two young kids in the house was challenging so he works most days in the office across town. He's been working a lot of hours—they're always on some sort of deadline—and I am frustrated with him for not spending time with the kids, for not coming home when he says he will, and for working even more hours after getting home in the evenings. I am so incredibly tired.

I look out the dining room window and see the lights of his car as he turns into the driveway. I feel my blood boiling. I don't get up. He comes into the house and barely acknowledges me and the kids. He doesn't apologize or ask me about my day. He goes to the office to set up his work computer as I get up and prepare him a plate of food. When he comes to the table, I am itching for a fight. I tell him I am tired. I ask why he didn't call if he was going to be late. He doesn't answer. I can tell he's thinking about work and not really there with us. I yell at him to answer me, and he looks at me like I'm crazy. I feel crazy. I tell him I can't do *this*, not really sure what I mean by my statement. I push back my chair, grab my purse and car keys, and storm out of the house, leaving him there with the kids.

I have to leave. I feel like I will die if I don't. I have no idea where I'm going, I just want to be away from my home, my husband, and my life. I am so mad I am shaking. I am filled with the energy that comes when one is in full fight-or-flight response. I drive mindlessly through our neighborhood and then in nearby neighborhoods, circling without intention. I cross the river and drive in old neighborhoods, imagining myself in a different life. I stop at a park and sit in my car for what feels like hours, waiting for the adrenalin to stop coursing through my veins. I can't think. I can't feel. I just want it all to stop. Eventually, fatigue takes over and I slowly make my way back home.

The dining table and the kitchen are still a mess. I drop my purse and keys and check on the girls who are tucked safely in their beds. I take a deep breath, then go to the kitchen and start cleaning. Tim is in the office working, as I knew he would be. We don't talk. I finish cleaning up and head upstairs to get ready for bed. I go to bed alone. I no longer wait for him to come to bed before letting the exhaustion take over, dropping into another restless night of much-needed sleep.

Escaping into Stories
December 2013 – One Year After Second Stroke

The gloominess of this rainy day matches my mood. It's mid-afternoon on a weekday. One of my daughters is taking a nap; the other one is noisily playing with her toys on the rug in front of me. I breathe a heavy sigh, grab my Kindle, turn it on, and drop into the book I am currently reading. It's escapist fiction of some sort. I'm not sure it matters what I read as long as it takes me away from being present to my own thoughts. Sometimes I use home shows or movies on TV as a way to escape, but since we are now keeping it screen-free for our daughters, I only do that at night when they're both asleep. Since one of my daughters no longer naps, I have turned to reading as my escape-of-choice during the day.

It's been a year since Tim's second stroke and, on most days, I officially hate my life. Tim and I are not getting along at all and, consequently, I am overwhelmed and frustrated most of the time. Our daughters are three years old now and have started attending a cooperative preschool, which has brought a little more joy and a whole lot of additional work for me. I suck it up and keep reminding myself of the benefits for our children.

We live in an old home, which I love, that was built in 1928. There isn't a family room, so the living room is littered with toys and books and shoes and clothes. I clean it up each night before bed and the mess comes right back the next day.

Today, one of my daughters is playing musical instruments and listening to music from the classes both of them attend each week. I feel waves of sadness and loneliness come over me and I stuff the feelings down. I don't have the bandwidth to be sad. I check the clock and realize I have a couple of hours before Tim will be home. Even though there is cleaning and organizing and cooking I could be doing, all I want to do is read. I look back down at my Kindle and focus on the book I'm reading. My daughter keeps banging away on her toy guitar and I tune out the noise as I escape into the story.

When I am home, I have discovered that escapism has become my outlet for loneliness. When the girls are playing, I will often read a book. When they are sleeping, I will typically watch a show on television. Home shows on HGTV are my favorite, but any movie will do. Anything to stay disconnected from my feelings.

I wonder if this form of escapism is normal for stay-at-home parents or if this behavior is tied to the overwhelming sense of loneliness that pervades my life.

I wonder if there will be a day when I will want to be *in* my life instead of escaping from it.

I wonder if there is a cure for loneliness that doesn't involve leaving my marriage.

Faking It

May 2014 – One Year and Six Months After Stroke

The air in the room is filled with tension. We are sitting separately in our therapist's office—Tim on an oversized black leather couch, me on a matching black chair. Our therapist completes the triangle by sitting in an office-style chair with his back to his desk. Tim and I are bringing years of frustration, pain, and sadness into the room with us.

It is our first couple's therapy session since the strokes. Tim is irritated and his whole body looks tense. I am a seething ball of anger. I am done. I want out. I want to end our marriage. I just want to walk away from all of it.

We tell our stories. I am matter-of-fact but find myself crying, telling the history of Tim's two strokes, his so-called recovery, and my frustration with his working late, his working on weekends, his focus on work, work, work and not at all on me and the kids. I share how that had been an issue early on in our relationship and how I made it clear to Tim that I did not want to be married to someone who was unwilling to spend any time with me.

In my head, I tell myself Tim is being an asshole.

In my head, I tell myself I want a divorce.

I listen as Tim reluctantly shares about his struggles to keep up at work. I listen as he shares about smiling, nodding, and faking his way through every day even though most of the time he has no idea what people are saying. I listen as he shares that he is afraid to tell anyone that he can't understand what they're saying. I listen as he shares that half the time when I speak to him, he has no idea what I am saying, so he either makes something up and reacts to that, or ignores me. I realize he is scrambling to hold on to his job and his identity as a software engineer—an identity that began when he was still a kid; an identity that was born out of deep love of doing the work. I listen and learn that he has come upon a problem that he cannot fix. He is drowning.

I sit there shocked. The tension in the air dissipates and a heavy cloud of grief settles in. I can't stop crying. I feel the weight of a ton of bricks fall onto my shoulders.

My husband isn't being an asshole. Frankly, that would be preferable. My husband simply hasn't recovered from his strokes. My husband is grasping to hang on to his identity as an engineer as strongly as I am grasping to hang on to our marriage.

He sits there wondering how long he can hold onto his career.

I sit here wondering how long we can hold onto our marriage.

Feeling Nothing at All

September 2014 – One Year and Ten Months After Second Stroke

We've been coming to couple's therapy for a few months and every week seems to reveal something new, another loss to explore, another pain to endure. Today is no exception. It's a lovely fall day and we are sitting in our usual seats—Tim on the couch and me in a chair to his left. Our therapist sits in his typical spot in a desk chair on my left. Each week I make the thirty-minute drive to this place near Tim's office, desperately hoping therapy will make things better in our marriage. Maybe I am also looking for a third party to let me know I'm not crazy.

About a year and a half ago one of our best friends was diagnosed with Stage 4 colon cancer and the whole situation has been rough. We were all supposed to grow old together. As I watch my marriage fall apart and our dear friend's health decline, I feel even more alone. I don't feel seen or held in my marriage as we move through this hell. I can't make sense of it, so it's hard to find the words to talk about it.

I take a deep breath and share about how I'm feeling and how alone I feel as we move through this difficult time. As Tim speaks of our friend's cancer diagnosis, his expression is completely flat and his words are without emotion. He makes a general comment about everyone having to die sometime. I am horrified. This is his best friend! His best friend who ended a vacation and jumped on a plane when Tim had his first stroke. His best friend who was there for Tim when Tim was hurting. This friend has been diagnosed with a cancer that may take his life and Tim is being all blasé about the whole thing. Inside I want to scream. Inside I want to yell at the therapist that this person sitting here on this sofa is not my husband. My husband has a heart and gives a shit about the people in his life and this *impersonator* is not my husband. I am so angry I am shaking. And then I do what I always do in therapy—I start crying.

The therapist asks about my tears and I cry harder.

My mind drifts back to a number of months ago when Tim's anxiety and depression had gotten so bad that he finally agreed to bring it up with his doctor. He did that and started a course of antidepressants. After about a month or so, his anxiety and depression got better. Hallelujah! I was so relieved. But then this other thing happened. He became emotionless, as if the medication had overcorrected somehow. It went from everything bothering him to nothing upsetting him at all. This has become more and more apparent as we watch our friend on his cancer journey.

I take a deep breath and sip a drink of water, willing my tears to stop. I share about Tim's lack of emotion or empathy and wonder if the antidepressant he is taking for his anxiety and depression could be taking away his access to feeling love, to feeling anything at all. His anxiety and depression have improved, which is good, but this emptiness I experience coming from him is disturbing and incongruent. I look at Tim. He is looking at me like I am a stranger. He seems unaffected by my distress. He seems unaffected by anything these days. I look at the therapist and his expression is one of grave concern, which lets me know I am not completely crazy.

After a lengthy discussion about anti-depressants and how different ones can affect people differently, Tim agrees to discuss the issue with his doctor. He says he doesn't see the need but agrees to do so anyway. I feel a huge wave of relief and sit back in my chair. I know he will follow through and I feel a tiny little spark of hope. I don't want him to feel anxious and depressed and I also don't want him to feel nothing at all.

Tim discussed the issue with his doctor. He was switched to a different antidepressant, which allowed him to have more access to his feelings. It didn't magically cure anything, but he was able to access feelings of sadness when our friend died from cancer a couple of months later. That may have been the first time I was grateful for feelings of grief.

Car Accidents
September 2014 – One Year and Ten Months After Second Stroke

I am standing in the dining room, setting the table, when I see Tim drive up the street and turn into our driveway. I gasp as he drives his car up the hill and parks. The front of the car has clearly been in an accident. He casually gets out of the car, walks up the sidewalk, and strides in through the front door. He looks normal. I ask what happened and if he is okay. He looks at me like he has no idea what I'm talking about. I point to the front of the car. He walks to the window and looks and seems shocked to see the damage.

I pull out a chair and sit down. I ask him to sit down and tell me what happened. He says he hit a car in front of him at a stop sign. He said they pulled off the road and there was no damage to the other car. The driver didn't want to pursue anything and they both drove away. Tim didn't even look at his car. Although he is now aware of the damage, he shrugs as if it is no big deal.

I look straight at him and ask, "What really happened?" not actually wanting to know. He's had several accidents over the past year. He misjudged the distance between my car and his on two different occasions, leaving long scratches down both sides of my car. We didn't pursue insurance. Then he hit a moving car while changing lanes. Thankfully our insurance took care of that one. He also hit the neighbor's trailer that was parked across the street. Once he hit a curb and blew a tire. The kids were in the car. I insisted he stop driving with the kids in the car after that incident. I can see a pattern emerging.

Tim answers my question by telling me he was practicing talking. *What the hell?* He often looks in a mirror to practice talking because lipreading helps him to know what words are actually coming out of his own mouth. It's a bizarre feedback loop that helps him with his aphasia. I look at him in horror and ask him if he was looking in the rearview mirror and practicing talking *while driving*. He admits he was. He says he was trying to figure out something he had said to someone at work. I am literally speechless.

I get up and finish making dinner, slamming things around in the kitchen and feeling completely helpless and overwhelmed. I know we will have to talk more about this at some point, but I have no idea what to say or do. I am worried about him. I am worried about his judgment. I am worried about his ability to make good decisions while driving a 3,500-pound vehicle. I can feel my world starting to unravel and I wonder if there is anything I can do to stop it all from being completely wrecked.

Asserting Control
December 2014 – Two Years After Second Stroke

The blanket around my legs feels warm as I sit on our cozy sofa. It's late evening and the girls are already in bed. Tim is in the office working and I am writing in my journal and trying to make some sense of my life. I keep trying to figure out what is so different this time around—after the second stroke. Why are things so different? Is it because we are parents now? Is it because I am not working outside the home? Is he different? Am I different? I keep writing, hoping to find some answers.

Tonight I am writing about control and how it is playing out currently in our marriage. I am starting to see a pattern of behavior that is disturbing to me. I write the following list and as I read it, the shock stops me in my tracks. It's as if I am writing about someone else. Not my husband. Not the man I fell in love with and married and chose to build a life with and chose to raise kids with. Not the man I have been in relationship with for the past twenty years. I blink back the tears and read the list again.

He follows behind me, redoing things I've done, such as moving the dishes around in the dishwasher after I have loaded it.

He ignores me and looks at his phone when I am talking to him, signaling the end of a conversation.

When I bring up things I want us to do as a family or things I want to do for myself, he says no, without discussion, as if he is now in charge.

He answers for the kids without waiting to hear what they have to say.

He yells at me, startling me each time, as raising his voice is out of character for him.

He yells at the kids for random things, leaving them confused by his behavior.

When I ask a question about something he brings up, he waves his phone within inches of my face, indicating he learned the information somewhere on there. He seems irritated when I ask him not to put his phone in my face.

When I ask a question about a computer issue, he moves my hands off the keyboard and takes over, instead of walking me through it, leaving me frustrated about his behavior and still confused about the computer issue.

He doesn't respect my privacy. For example, if I have a friend over, he sits in the room with us while we visit.

I stare at the list. I know everyone has bad behavior at times. I know that each of these things individually may not be a big deal, but when I see them all together and know that each of them has happened many times, I am stunned. This is not the Tim I have known. None of these behaviors are consistent with the man I have been with for the past two decades. Some of these behaviors *never* happened before the second stroke. What the hell happened to my husband? What the hell did those blood clots do to his personality, to who he is?

Sometimes there are big things that take a relationship to its knees, and sometimes there are little things that happen over and over and creep inside a relationship and destroy it. And sometimes there is a brain injury that happens and you discover the person you used to know is gone and there is a completely different person in his place.

I close my journal and cry, knowing in my heart that someone or something has to change.

Fast-Food Escape
December 2014 – Two Years After Second Stroke

I smell the fries, feel my mouth start to water, and experience a loosening of the tension in my body. I'm in my car in the drive-thru line at a local fast-food restaurant ordering my dinner. My daughters are with me, buckled in their car seats in the back. I know I should be home cooking something healthy, but I just can't do it. I order the food, knowing it will taste good in the moment and that I will likely regret it shortly thereafter. I order it anyway. I order chicken nuggets for the kids, which I will serve to them with rice and raw vegetables at home. I refuse to give them the greasy fries and congratulate myself for being less awful to my kids than to myself. I completely avoid the kid's meals, knowing they would probably like the toys, but we don't need any more plastic crap in our house.

It's been a couple of years since the second stroke and life is busy and overwhelming. The girls are in the co-op preschool a couple of mornings a week, Tim is still working long hours, and I am still angry at him most of the time. I thought preschool would give me a little break, but I was wrong. I have to volunteer and take on a couple of "jobs" as part of our payment to the school, which leaves me feeling even more overwhelmed.

I manage to provide healthy meals for myself and for my kids for breakfast and lunch. In contrast to this, I am refusing to cook dinner for Tim or myself and have been getting fast food multiple times per week for myself. Tim is on his own for dinner and, most nights, he makes himself a sandwich. I am humiliated by this behavior, and I can't seem to stop. I am struggling. I keep trying to be a good mom and a good wife and a good friend and a good person and I just don't have the energy or the motivation to keep at it. So, I eat. It helps. It numbs the pain for a short while and helps me get to the next task without losing my cool or losing my mind.

I take the bag of yummy-smelling garbage food and wonder if this will be my last time here.

I wonder what it is going to take for me to stop this behavior.

A year later I finally got up the courage to reach out for support from a health coach who I met at the preschool. She was a lifeline. I was able to shift gears at that time and focus more on my health, letting go of the fast-food habit, taking one tiny step toward loving myself.

Protection at Work
February 2015 – Two Years and Two Months After Second Stroke

The energy in the room is heavy and filled with sadness and anger. Our daughters are asleep and Tim and I are sitting in the living room of our beautiful old home having a frank discussion about our future. Tim is going out on medical leave for the third time and it looks like this time it will be permanent. He recently opened up to me about his challenges at work, his challenges with understanding spoken and written language, and his fear of being seen as stupid. He shares how he works late every night and on the weekends in order to try to catch up and make some sense of the projects he's been assigned—projects he would have been leading in the past. He knows his brain isn't functioning the way it did before.

Tim has wanted to work with computers since he was a teenager. His career has long been his happy place. He loves it. The stress of him ending his career in his mid-fifties in this way is heartbreaking, terrifying, and infuriating. I am experiencing many feelings, anger bubbling to the top of the heap most of the time. I am mad at his work for not protecting him. I'm mad at Tim for hiding the truth from me, and I am mad at myself for not knowing.

Back in 2008, Tim was given an indefinite leave of absence after his first stroke. He went back to work about eighteen months later and was doing well until he had the second stroke late in 2012. After his second stroke, Tim and his manager apparently had several conversations that Tim didn't fully understand. Tim says he pretended he understood so he wouldn't look bad. His employer didn't communicate with me, so I had no idea there were concerns or challenges happening at work. His manager talked to him about the possibility of moving from a senior position to a junior position due to his performance. His manager offered to get HR involved, implying that Tim had other options. Tim chose the demotion. He didn't understand that he could have been evaluated for long-term disability at that point. He thought he would be fired if he didn't take the demotion. None of this was communicated to him in writing, despite the fact that he had aphasia. (This cues my anger.)

He continued to work and continued to struggle at work until it became clear that he could no longer effectively do his job. Human Resources finally got involved. He made the decision to go out on medical leave and be fully evaluated for long-term disability. He was assessed and deemed unable to do his job, *or any job,* and left his career, receiving disability benefits based on a junior engineer's salary after working in the field for more than thirty years.

The anger continues to roll through me.

I am angry that Tim wasn't protected at work.

I am angry that as his caregiver I didn't know enough to protect him.

Loss of Identity
February 2015 – Two Years and Two Months After Stroke

I am in the basement sorting through boxes of old papers and books, trying to clear out some clutter before we put the house on the market. Since we have lived in this house for almost twenty years, we have collected a whole lot of stuff. It's mid-morning on a weekday and I'm going through a box of papers and books from Tim's college days. He says he doesn't want any of it, but I am hesitant to chuck it without looking through it first. I am definitely the collector in the family.

As I go through a box to sort out what can be recycled, I set aside a few things Tim wrote years ago and some papers I think may be interesting to him. While sorting, I find more than twenty letters from some of the top colleges and universities in the country, all offering him acceptance into their graduate programs. I am shocked. These are not easy schools to get into. He has never mentioned this. Not once has he ever boasted about being pursued in this way. Not once. The letters are all dated just after he graduated from college with degrees in electrical engineering and computer science.

I grab the letters and head up the stairs to the living room where Tim is drinking a cup of coffee and watching the kids play. I ask him about the stack of letters I'm holding in my hand, and he says he never wanted to go to graduate school so he just ignored them. He says he is surprised he even kept them. He says he wanted to be done with school and go to work.

I am speechless.

I turn and head back to the basement and reluctantly toss the letters into the bag of recycling. The heaviness I feel in my chest is huge. The weight of his loss is overwhelming. His identity is so intertwined with his work with computers. Because of the challenges caused by his two large strokes, he has had to give up that dream, that identity. Who is he without that identity?

No wonder he is angry.

No wonder he is depressed.

Throughout life we all collect identities. Some of them are keepers, some of them can be chucked out like old papers. How do we find our bearings when an identity is stripped away? This may be the first time I can truly relate to Tim's pain. We have both had identities stripped away and new identities assigned that were not of our choosing. We are both struggling to find our footing in a world that is dramatically shifting beneath us.

Years later, I find myself thinking a lot about caregivers and identity. It's interesting how I, as a caregiver, willingly (and with much resentment) gave up my own identity in an effort to help my husband find his way back to his identity that was shattered by his brain injuries. I can see how I was primed as a woman to take on this role. I can see how my identity became inextricably tied to his well-being at the expense of my own.

It makes sense to me now why there are high rates of depression for caregivers. We are shamed by ourselves and others if we choose not to shed our own identity when we care for a loved one. The expectations are crushing.

Leaving Home
July 2015 – Two Years and Seven Months After Second Stroke

I stand in the living room of this beautiful home that is no longer mine and watch as the movers take our belongings out the front door to the moving truck. Our daughters are standing at the front window, watching the action with complete fascination. To them, this is an adventure, something exciting and new. To me, it is simply another loss.

Our house is not just a house, a home, a dwelling. It is a dynamic, living, breathing scrapbook of the almost twenty years we have lived here. Every room, every surface, every plant in the yard holds a memory. Every moment here has a page in the scrapbook—some significant, like marriage and babies coming home; some mundane, like the sound of the trash cans being rolled down to the street each week; and some traumatic, like the paramedics and firefighters filling the house the night of Tim's first stroke.

I never thought of our home as temporary. When we bought it we talked about being here until we were really old. If I'd known we'd one day be moving, I would have loved it differently, like a summer fling in college—all in, but not really. Sadly, in this house, I was all in.

We are moving to the suburbs. We are moving for better-funded, more diverse schools and we are also moving to scale back our lifestyle to better accommodate Tim being permanently disabled. I am constantly flipping back and forth between hope for the future and the grief of what we are leaving behind. We are leaving a neighborhood we love, friends we've known for decades, and a home that was once so filled with joy.

We sold our "forever" home and, surprisingly, found another one we could begin to love, maybe another living scrapbook for our future.

I used to think selling a home would be like a divorce—a breakup that leaves everyone feeling rejected in some way. When selling our home, that metaphor didn't land at all. There is a ton of grief, but it doesn't feel like rejection. As I stand here in tears, watching them load the moving truck, I wonder if home ownership is more like a foster situation. We are "gifted" a home for a time, and we do our very best to nurture, love, and prepare it for the next family who will be "gifted" with it. When the parting day comes, we put on a brave face and lovingly say good-bye to the home that has crawled inside our hearts. That parting day is today and all I feel is overwhelming waves of grief.

I walk through all the rooms of this beloved house and wonder if maybe, just maybe, this extraordinary home was fostering us.

I Am Not Your Mother
July 2015 – *Two Years and Seven Months After Second Stroke*

We are sitting in our therapist's office on a warm summer day, still trying to hammer out some of the challenges between us. It's been more than two years since Tim's second stroke, and we are focusing on being truly honest with each other about our feelings, frustrations, and resentments. These are not easy conversations for either of us. As usual, Tim is heavily armored up. The strokes have taken away so much of his identity and confidence. I am struggling with the sense of failing as a caregiver and a wife and, as a result, often feel like a pretty shitty human being. Our therapist lovingly holds this tender space for both of us.

Today I bring up my frustration with feeling like my husband expects me to mother him. I don't want to be his mother—I want to be his wife, his partner—and I am so full of resentment for being relegated to the mother role. Tim shares that he is equally frustrated with me and doesn't want to be mothered by me. I roll my eyes and sigh, irritated as he throws this back in my face.

Our therapist kindly invites us to spend a week consciously *not* engaged in these roles and see what happens. I agree not to mother Tim, and he agrees not to pull on me to do so.

It's now a week later and we are back in our therapist's office. Tim sits on the couch and I sit in a big black chair, both of us armored up as usual. The week was sadly illuminating. Tim shares that he does, in fact, need me to be there for him in a mothering way. He doesn't want to call it mothering, but it is what he wants and needs from me. He needs me to tell him what to do. He wants me to take care of him. As he says this, I feel hot tears roll down my cheeks.

This is not the marriage I want to have.

Impact of Caregiving on Health
November 2015 – Two Years and Eleven Months After Second Stroke

I like that my naturopath talks to me in her office rather than in an exam room. It's much more comfortable to have a conversation when I am fully dressed, and I appreciate this little act of grace. She sits calmly across from me in a sunny office full of beautiful plants. I have been having some health issues and today I am hoping to finally get some answers. We are discussing the results of my recent medical tests, reviewing my medical records, and coming up with a plan. She thoughtfully answers all my questions in language I can understand and doesn't rush me.

I started experiencing some health challenges shortly after Tim's first stroke, back in 2008. Mostly I ignored them. I didn't have time to be sick. I powered on, powered through. This worked for a number of years and now the strategy isn't working so well. I have been feeling "off" for a while, struggling with digestive issues, insomnia, back pain, and exhaustion. I had a colonoscopy, thinking the test would provide some answers. It didn't. The gastroenterologist sent me a letter saying everything looked great and I should come back in ten years. I was shattered. I did not feel seen. My words, my concerns, my physical health challenges were invisible to him. I was so angry. I stuffed the anger inside and continued ignoring my health. That went on for a number of months before the discomfort in my body started impacting my ability to function well. At that point, I did some research and found a naturopath who specialized in working with women with digestive issues and decided to give the medical profession another try.

As I listen to my doctor talk about my results, it's clear that I'm not making this shit up. My body is experiencing a number of health-related challenges. I am anemic. I have adrenal fatigue. My vitamin D level is low. I have become extremely intolerant to a number of foods—some of which I have been consuming on a regular basis. As the naturopath goes over all the results of the bloodwork, I feel the puzzle pieces falling into place and hope starts to bloom.

My doctor looks right at me and asks, with a very serious tone of voice, how I manage to get through an ordinary day. I start to cry. I can't remember the last time I felt so seen. I let her know I am pushing through the fatigue and digestive distress because I don't have any other choice. I am a mom. I am a wife to someone who is disabled. I am a caregiver and I don't have the option of tapping out.

She very kindly and very firmly tells me this behavior of pushing through has to stop. She says if I keep this up, there will come a day where I won't have the energy to get out of bed. For some reason, in this sunny office with this kind doctor, the words get through.

I'm done ignoring my health.

It's time for me to step into being a caregiver of myself.

Home Depot
May 2016 – *Three Years and Five Months After Second Stroke*

It's a spring day and Tim and I are on a little shopping adventure with our kids. We are at our local Home Depot store looking for a cotter pin to fix a bathtub stopper. It's a little like looking for a needle in a haystack.

Tim is pushing the shopping cart as I slowly scan the aisles for the part; neither one of us is very good at asking for help. The hardware aisle is crowded with lots of people who are probably also looking for tiny random parts. Our daughters are bored. As usual, the outing sounded more interesting than this standing, scanning, and waiting.

An elderly man with a cane comes shuffling by and I gently move the shopping cart out of his way, pulling it toward me so he has room to pass. Tim starts yelling at me. In the store. In front of the kids. He yells at me for trying to take his cart. He yells at me for controlling him. His face is red, his voice is loud, and I can feel the intensity of his anger. I am stunned. I am dumbstruck.

I deliberately walk over, take the girls by their hands, and quickly walk out of the store. I don't say a word. I leave him there with the cart and I don't look back. In my head, this moment is the final straw. Verbally abusing me in front of our daughters in a public place is over the proverbial line. Disability or not. Enough.

I am shaking as we head to the car. We get in and wait. The girls are unusually quiet. They are barely six years old. I take a deep breath and tell them everything will be okay. I say that daddy and mommy are having a disagreement and we will work it out.

He finally comes out and gets in the car. He calmly buckles his seat belt and looks at me. I stare at him and feel my blood boiling. He looks perplexed and says, "I can't believe you left me in there. What happened?" I tell him coolly and directly he is *never* to speak to me like that again, anywhere, ever.

When he says he has no idea what I am talking about, I feel my anger dissolve into a puddle of sadness. I can tell from the look on his face that he is telling the truth. He doesn't even remember what happened in the store a few minutes ago. I am speechless again as I turn and start the car.

Brain injuries are assholes.

People with Disabilities
May 2016 – Three Years and Five Months After Second Stroke

My daughters and I take seats at an outdoor table at our local Starbucks, preparing to soak up some sun while enjoying a sugary treat. It's a sunny Wednesday afternoon in late spring and I am grateful we got here before the middle school up the road lets out. When that happens, the outdoor tables are quickly taken over by students. The girls are sharing about their fun day in kindergarten and I am people-watching and enjoying some time away from the house.

I notice a man sitting alone at the table next to us. He is probably in his sixties and has a cane propped against his table. His right arm looks like it's stuck in the bent position—something that is common after strokes due to paralysis. I wonder if he had a stroke. A few people come by and chat with him. He can only say a few words—he clearly has aphasia—but he is friendly and has a smile that lights up his whole face when people stop by.

Tim was always the one in our relationship who could talk to anyone. I am more of the observer, the watcher, the introverted one. As I sit here with our kids, I think about their dad and how often Tim is ignored or treated poorly because of his disabilities. I take a deep breath, stand up, and walk over to the table where the man is sitting. I introduce myself and my daughters. I share that my husband had a stroke and has aphasia. I ask if that is what happened to him as well. He nods and shares some of his story. He can only say yes and no verbally but is able to write additional responses on a piece of paper. The girls and I move to his table and talk with him in this way for about thirty minutes. I find out that he comes to this location every Wednesday after physical therapy and I offer to introduce him to my husband the following week. He is delighted.

I was taught not to stare at people who are different, which in turn taught me to completely ignore people who have visible differences, including disabilities. I have seen the impact of this kind of behavior on Tim. I have watched people speak loudly to him because he doesn't understand, as if yelling the same words will make him understand. I have watched him be ignored. I have watched people roll their eyes when he takes too long to get out a sentence. Today I am stuffing down all that old learning and am choosing to model something different for my children. Today I am showing my daughters how to treat people with dignity and respect regardless of their differences.

The following week, Tim joined the girls and me at Starbucks and I made the introductions to our new friend. Tim and that man became fast friends and started attending an aphasia support group together a couple of times per month. My kids still ask about him and say hello to him when we see him out in the community.

Heart Walk

May 2016 – Three Years and Five Months After Second Stroke

slowly drive my van into a large grassy field, following the directions of the signs and the attendants as I move toward a parking spot. The field is being used as a makeshift parking lot for hundreds of cars. People of all ages from all walks of life are slowly moving from the cars toward tents, booths, and a large stage set up down the road. It feels like a pilgrimage of some sort. It's early morning on a beautiful spring day and even though it's a little chilly, I think it's going to be a warm day, a perfect day for a walk.

Even though I love to hike and walk, I haven't participated in an organized walk or run since that day back in 1994 when I ran a 5K on the same day as my first date with Tim. I'm not really sure why I haven't participated in one since. That's another story.

As I climb out of my car and head for the tables where I will check in and get my number, I am overwhelmed with emotion. I blink back tears and take a few deep breaths to calm myself. Today I am walking in a 5K to raise money for the American Heart Association—the organization most known for its long history of helping to fight against heart disease and stroke.

The last time I showed up for an organized race, I was excited to be meeting up with friends. I felt good about raising money for a cause I believed in, and I was filled with anticipation, knowing that later that day I would be going on a first date with someone I had been crushing on for months. That nervous energy was perfect for a run. I needed to move.

Today I am also experiencing a vast array of emotions, but this time it's very different. This time the race is personal. I am walking to raise money for a cause that has touched my life in such a profoundly intimate way. I am walking to raise money for survivors like my husband, and for all the caregivers who are both blessed and cursed to be caring for their loved ones. I am walking to raise money for all the people who have been crushed by grief and loss.

A few months ago I heard about the Heart Walk and decided to participate. I didn't seek approval. I didn't talk anyone into doing it with me. I just wanted to do this thing on my own. I wanted to do something on my own that wasn't being asked of me.

I reached out to friends and family and gathered sponsors and I showed up. I showed up.

This event is being held at a lovely location on the outskirts of the city. There are both paved and gravel roads near a stream mostly shaded by trees. It is absolutely beautiful. It is so heartwarming and heartbreaking to see so many people show up in wheelchairs, on scooters, with walkers, and with canes—all walking to raise money for research. There is something magical about the power of a collective.

I put on my number and wander around people-watching, knowing everyone here has some sort of story similar to mine or Tim's. Either they or someone they love has been impacted by stroke or heart disease. I feel waves and waves of emotion roll through me. I need to move. When the walk starts, I am so grateful to be in motion. The emotions need somewhere to go. Movement helps. I keep to myself. I don't talk to anyone. I just feel and move and feel and move and feel and move, praying for relief to come.

As I walk, I am carrying a cardboard sign that looks like a torch, with Tim's name written on it. I find it ironic that in my last race, I was "carrying a torch" for Tim and today I am carrying a fake cardboard torch in his honor, and my crush on him is most definitely gone.

I wonder if caregivers always find ways to carry torches for those we love, even when that love has changed or gone.

Insanity Rules
July 2016 – Three Years and Seven Months After Second Stroke

I swear under my breath as I sit at my kitchen table compiling a list of language-related challenges caused by Tim's first and second strokes. I am using my own experience and notes from his various providers to create the list. I am so damned angry right now and am trying to channel my emotion into something useful.

Receptive aphasia

Expressive aphasia

Limited ability to process language

Easily frustrated when unable to understand language

I just got off the phone with someone at the Social Security office and I can feel my blood boiling. Tim has had two neuropsychiatric evaluations—one for Social Security and one for the insurance company that pays his long-term disability benefits. Both companies have refused to share the results of these neuro-psych exams with us or with any of Tim's medical practitioners. The psychologists who conducted the evaluations report they are not able to share the results, as they were contracted to do them and have not been given permission to share. I can feel smoke coming out of my ears.

Difficulty reading

Difficulty writing

Significant difficulty with numbers—both when he hears them and when he speaks them

Difficulty understanding language when anxious or upset

While we are grateful for the benefits Tim receives from these two entities, their refusal to share this information is mind-boggling. When I requested the information be shared, their response was that they paid for the evaluations so they own the results. I want to scream. I understand they paid for the evaluators' time, but this is Tim's life—his words, his challenges, his well-being, his cross to bear. They clearly don't give a shit about his actual life.

Difficulty understanding long sentences

Difficulty understanding complex words

Difficulty understanding when words are spoken quickly

Difficulty focusing on more than one thing at a time

All we were told was that Tim was unable to do his job, *or any job,* and he was approved for permanent disability benefits. That was the extent of it. After two entire days of testing, that was all the information we were given. Not what might be helpful. Not what kind of therapy might make his life better. Not what kind of support might help him through his incredible loss. Nothing. I was sarcastically told that Tim could schedule his own neuropsychiatric assessment. I looked into it and it is not covered by our insurance and would cost several thousand dollars. Great.

Difficulty understanding when multiple people are speaking, as in a group setting or at a dinner table

Often needs extra time to understand what's been said and gets confused when the speaker keeps talking

Often has difficulty finding the right word or words to express an idea (word on the tip of the tongue phenomenon)

Difficulty prioritizing

Tim had to go to the state of Washington for his second neuropsych evaluation, as the insurance company and Social Security were unwilling to use the same report. When the second evaluation was scheduled, it was set up by the insurance company with a contractor in the Seattle area—more than three hours away from our home in the Portland, Oregon, area. Even though there are multiple providers of this service in our city, I was told they were not an option.

Tim couldn't drive that far on his own and I was home with two small children. The test took close to eight hours, so doing it three hours away required an overnight stay at a hotel. The insurance company paid for the hotel, but we were on our own for transportation. Fortunately, one of our friends was willing to drive Tim to Washington. I can't wrap my head around this being required of a client with multiple brain injuries. What about people who don't have friends or family who can help out?

Sometimes confuses words

Sometimes uses words out of order—significant with the use of pronouns

Sometimes speaks without providing context and struggles to provide context when asked

Difficulty understanding language when there is background noise

Depressed due to loss of language abilities

I take a deep breath and release it. I take another deep breath, willing myself to calm down. I add a few more things to my list, wondering where to turn for additional support. I know that we are on our own to find the support we need to cope with the challenges. I know that I can't stay in this angry place or nothing will happen. I make another list, this time of support persons—those we've accessed already and those who may be useful in the future.

Speech therapist

Psychotherapist

Support group for stroke survivors

Support group for people with aphasia

Psychotherapist who specializes in working with people with disabilities

Primary Care Physician

Friends

Family

I know I can't do this alone. The insanity of bureaucratic rules will not stop me from reaching out for the support we so desperately need right now.

My days of shouldering this caregiving load alone are over.

No More Pretending

September 2016 – Three Years and Nine Months After Stroke

I am driving my minivan on yet another boring errand, thinking about the groceries I need to buy and half listening to the constant chatter of my two lively six-year-olds in the backseat. I am shocked to full attention when one of my daughters asks me if her dad and I are going to get unmarried.

Huh, what?

She goes on to say that maybe if we got unmarried, we wouldn't fight so much.

Thud. My heart drops into my stomach. Out of the mouths of babes. I burn with shame as the moment sears into my brain. I take a mental snapshot of the exact spot where I am on that tree-lined street, facing south, preparing to make a left turn. I feel the slowing of time and the gravity of her words as I continue to drive.

Tim and I have been struggling in our marriage for a long while and I thought we were doing a great job of keeping our challenges away from our kids. We've been going to couple's therapy, discussing all of our options, and still find ourselves to be pretty miserable most of the time. In our effort to protect our kids, we failed to see how much they pick up through our emotional energy.

Damn.

Something needs to change.

It hits me that I am the one who needs to make the change.

How Can I Leave?
October 2016 – Three Years and Ten Months After Second Stroke

We are a couple of years into weekly couple's therapy appointments, trying to find the way through or the way out. We sit in our usual spots—Tim on the couch, me several feet away in a black overstuffed chair, a large box of tissues nearby. I smell the lavender tea on the table beside me. I feel the tension in the room and my husband's frustration, and I feel all the walls go up in my body. I keep thinking, *How can I leave? I took vows. He's disabled, for God's sake. Until death. In sickness and in health. How can I leave? I took vows. Marriage vows. I meant them with every fiber of my being. When I give my word, it means something. Breaking my word to someone is never okay.* I say none of this.

Week after week, I think, *How can I leave?* and then say nothing.

This particular day is nothing special. Another day in the journey of a bunch of tough years. I am talking about integrity as I continue to ignore my own needs and wants. My husband sits stoically, staring at me as I weep and ramble on about nothing of relevance while obsessively thinking, *How can I leave?*

Our therapist looks at each of us and calmly asks a question: "Did you take vows to make each other miserable?" Again. "Did you take vows to make each other miserable?"

Something clicks and settles deep inside me; something that shifts everything. I start to cry as I am finally able to whisper, "No." I now see a truth deeper than our vows—the truth that I am not here to make myself or another person miserable.

I finally see that breaking my word may be the kindest thing I can do.

That day we turned a corner and began the heartbreaking and beautiful unraveling of the most painful parts of our marriage. We revisited our vows and committed to those we could hold and said goodbye to those that no longer felt true. We committed to living in the best interest of our children and each other. It wasn't easy and it wasn't wrong.

Puppy Training
November 2016 – Three Years and Eleven Months After Second Stroke

The tension in the house is high and we are all on edge most of the time. It's the middle of a weekday. The girls are in school and I'm upstairs trying to do some much-needed cleaning in their room while they are away. Tim and I have been separated for about a month now and have moved to separate bedrooms to see if we can peacefully coexist while living *separately* under the same roof. It's not ideal and it's certainly not peaceful.

Zoey, our five-month-old puppy, is downstairs whining at the door to go outside. I know Tim is down there, so I take a deep breath and ignore the whining. Zoey continues to whine. I give up and stomp down the stairs. As I walk into the family room, I see Tim sitting on the couch a few feet away from the back door. The dog is standing right in front of the door, peeing on the floor. I lose my mind. I ask him why the hell he didn't let the dog out. He says he didn't know why she was whining. I look at him like he has two heads and yell, "What the fuck did you think she wanted?" I grab some paper towels and cleanser and angrily clean up the mess, muttering swear words the entire time. He continues to passively sit on the couch, ignoring me and the dog.

After I clean up the mess, I put on my coat, pick up the dog and go out into the backyard, slamming the door for good measure. I am so mad I'm shaking. As the adrenalin wears off, I start to cry. I wander around the yard crying, following our puppy, hoping the walking will bring some relief. I'm annoyed with Tim. I'm frustrated with myself for losing my temper. I'm concerned about my yelling. This is not me. This is not like me. I don't like the person I am becoming. I wonder if our dog will ever be properly potty-trained or if we will just keep giving her mixed messages and have to clean up after her forever. I wonder how much of the tension in the house the kids are absorbing.

I pick up the dog and head back into the house. I am relieved to see that Tim is no longer sitting in the family room. It's disturbing how angry I am at him. It's disturbing how uncomfortable I now feel in my own home.

Maybe the time has come for us to live *separately* under separate roofs.

When Did They Become My Kids?
December 2016 – Four Years After Second Stroke

I ramble on about my life and hear myself saying those words again: *my kids*. Somewhere along the way I started referring to our daughters as *my kids*, not *our kids*. I am sitting in my therapist's office on a cold winter day exploring what the hell it means. It's complicated. Tim and I have been separated for a couple of months. Maybe this language is preparation for our new, even more separate lives. Maybe it's mamabear protective energy flying out of me to combat what is happening in our family right now. I honestly don't know.

I remember back to an adoption class Tim and I took about a decade ago. In the class we talked about that point when someone becomes a parent. It was about as clear as mud. We weren't pregnant in the traditional sense, but at the time of that class we were waiting for a phone call for one child and on a waiting list for another. We had been chosen to be adoptive parents by a birthmother when she was a couple of months away from giving birth.

Did we become parents when we were chosen to be our daughter's parents?

Did we become parents when we held our baby girl in our arms on the day she was born?

Did we become parents when the courts said we were?

It turns out there are no absolutely correct answers; it's all arbitrary. There are legal definitions and personal definitions. For me, the moment I knew *of* my daughters, I knew they were my children. I knew I was their mom. At that moment, I became their parent and they became *my kids*.

Once our daughters came home, they became *our* kids. Our children. And then, as things started to unravel between me and Tim after the second stroke, I found myself saying *my* daughters and *my kids* more and more often, even when talking to Tim. Each time I said it, I was shocked and even embarrassed by my own words.

I blink away the memories, shifting uncomfortably in my chair. I take an extra deep breath and open up to my therapist, sharing those thoughts and memories with him.

I am so tired of living in the land of make believe—the land where Tim and I live happily ever after with our children who are not at all impacted by the shitshow that was our marriage.

I am ready to fully step into the land of truth.

Separation News

December 2016 – Four Years After Second Stroke

I am exhausted and sad and so ready to not feel exhausted and sad all the time. It's the day after Christmas and Tim and I are sitting in our family room having another conversation about our relationship, about the vows we have decided to set aside. The girls are upstairs playing with new toys acquired on Christmas Day. We decide it is finally time to formally tell our families about our separation.

We made the decision to finally end our marriage a couple of months ago and have told our children and a few friends but have not yet shared the decision with our extended families. We hinted about it in our annual holiday letter but have not yet come right out and spoken our truth. We are currently living in the same home but are no longer living as married. Since communicating by phone is still a challenge for Tim, I agree to write a letter and Tim will give feedback and we will make changes until it feels right to both of us. Surprisingly, we work pretty well together on this project.

I have spent years judging myself around making a decision to end our marriage. I am finally in a grounded place where I know I am making the best decision for myself, for Tim, and for our children. I am no longer willing to entertain any additional advice, judgment, or feedback. This has to be in the first paragraph. I am clearly setting a boundary around our decision, and it feels empowering.

I hope that when we put the decision to formally end our marriage behind us, we will finally be able to move on with grieving all of the losses we have endured over the past nine years.

When someone becomes disabled due to brain injuries, the disability is often invisible. Tim's loss of the ability to express and understand language is still so often unseen by those around him. This leaves him (and me) without the support we need for the grief that hangs in the air every single day. I often hear things like "His recovery is such a blessing," "He is so lucky," and "You must be so grateful." When I hear things like this I want to scream obscenities. I don't. Instead I lash out at the world, at God, and at myself. At least divorce is a fairly tangible loss. I wonder if people will respond more thoughtfully. I won't hold my breath.

Fast forward one week...

We sent the letter a week ago and today I am filled with rage. The pushback has been painful. The impact of our family members hating one of us and loving the other is astounding. I take a deep breath and blow it all out. I send blessings to myself and others. I try to understand where they are coming from and how their own fears and their own experiences may be influencing their actions. Mostly I just feel confused and abandoned in this very dark time.

I vow not to take this frustration out on Tim. He's been through enough.

I vow not to take this frustration out on myself. I've also been through enough.

The letter:

Dear Families,

I'm guessing that the news of Tim and I splitting—after being together for twenty-two years—was somewhat of a shock to some of you. Some of you have seen the struggles all along and we have greatly appreciated your incredible support. Some of you have reached out recently with questions and concerns and this letter is an attempt to answer some questions and respond to your concerns. We are not soliciting advice but welcome and appreciate your support.

Tim and I had a very successful and wonderful marriage. This is not a failure. The first fourteen years we were together were some of the best years of my life and of his. We had careers we loved, the love of friends and family, a home in a neighborhood we loved, and we were so so excited to start a family. When Tim's first stroke happened, it knocked the wind out of us, but we persevered. His recovery was so incredible and somewhat "miraculous" given how large his stroke was, and we were ever so hopeful. We put our family plans on hold and focused solely on his recovery. When he returned to work, we threw our hat back in the ring for the adoption and moved forward. Life was still pretty good, and we were still very focused on his recovery.

Our first daughter was such a blessing, and we were so excited to be parents. Tim's recovery had slowed some and his receptive aphasia was still pretty problematic, but we were still so hopeful and kept expecting a "full recovery." We moved forward with the second adoption and continued to be hopeful about his recovery and the future. When the second stroke happened, everything changed.

There are lots of variables, so I don't want to pin it all on one thing. Tim's personality was significantly different after two major strokes. He became very introverted and many of his interests changed. His mood was also dramatically different. We had two very small children—one who was still adjusting to her new family and home. Tim was struggling at work and wasn't aware of his employment options and I wasn't aware he was struggling. Tim's anxiety and depression were signif-

icant, and he tried medication, counseling, support groups and nothing seemed to help much. I struggled to adjust to a husband who was so dramatically different, and our relationship became more and more toxic.

We both kept thinking things would get better and eventually we would get our old marriage back. In May of 2014, we started marriage counseling. We are still going, two and a half years later. It has helped us immensely to get through some incredibly tough transitions with Tim leaving work due to his aphasia, us moving to a new neighborhood, and then deciding to end our marriage. Tim is also working with a psychologist who is a disability specialist.

We are hopeful that a more structured, less chaotic environment will be beneficial for Tim and that, in turn, I will be in an environment that is more healthy for me and the kids. We are planning to sell our home and buy a condo for Tim and a small home for me and the girls. Our hope is to have the houses be within walking distance or a short drive and we will continue to co-parent to the best of our abilities.

We are doing this lovingly and in the best interests of ourselves and our children. We are friends and will remain friends. Despite ending the marriage, I will not abandon Tim. He is the father of my children. He didn't do anything wrong. The strokes were not his fault. We were dealt a hand that made our marriage worse, not better, and we are going to do what we can to ensure that our kids have a loving relationship with him.

Our situation is far from "normal," so we are basically making our own road map. Our family won't end up looking "normal," but we will still be a family and we are both committed to keeping it that way.

Tim had his first stroke in 2008, so we've been working on this for a long, long time. We are not making snap decisions and we are not rushing through any of this. We will continue to work with our marriage counselor and our financial advisor and an attorney to make sure we make decisions that are the best for all of us.

Please let me know if you have questions. We are both willing to talk about this and appreciate your kindness and support.

Love, Devon (and Tim)

Witnessing Grief
February 2017 – Four Years and Two Months After Second Stroke

I sip from my cup of lavender tea and cry as I sit in my therapist's office in my usual chair. After a few years of couple's therapy, I decided it was finally time to go to individual therapy and start dealing with my giant ball of grief. I haven't had therapy for myself since the less-than-stellar experience a few years ago. Even though I am a psychotherapist myself, I am shocked at how skeptical I am about whether or not it will actually help me.

I come to each session, start talking, and then cry for the majority of the fifty-minute hour. Today is no exception. I start to cry. I do my best to fight back the tears as my therapist encourages the feelings to come. I sit and cry. Ugly crying, with tears and snot and mascara running down my face. I am embarrassed. I feel as if I am doing something wrong, wondering how I am ever going to make progress if all I ever do is cry.

My therapist doesn't judge. He allows the tears and the rage and the sadness and the confusion and the pain and the anger and the grief to flow through my tears and fill the room around us. I empty it all out onto the floor. Then I wipe my face, blow my nose, and schedule to meet again in a few weeks, trusting I have emptied enough of the despair to keep on living for a while.

Several years after that experience, after many more therapy sessions, I received a call from a friend who was in a deep state of grief. Almost every part of me wanted to jump in and try to fix it, make them feel better, distract them from their pain.

I also wanted to take myself out of the discomfort of being with them in their pain. And yet, there was a tiny little part of me that reminded myself to be there, just be there, and witness and honor the pain. I was being given an opportunity—a gift—to witness the grief of a dear friend in a completely new way. So I shut my mouth and listened and held space and wrapped my friend in an imaginary blanket of healing. What I experienced in that moment surprised me. It was the purest form of love. I didn't fall into a dark place. It didn't hurt to be there. I moved into a state of being that was different, something unexpected, something truly precious.

It reminded me of all those hours in my therapist's office. All those hours of having my own grief be witnessed. That was my healing. It wasn't the talking, the processing, or the under-standing why. It was the witnessing of my grief.

I read about this in David Kessler's books and the books of countless others. I heard about this in workshops and in my training, but, surprisingly, it wasn't until that phone call with a friend that it all circled around and fell into complete alignment in my mind.

I think about how I kept my grief hidden away from my friends and family and only shared a fraction of what I was feeling. It was complicated. I wanted to be optimistic and upbeat about Tim's recovery, our new family, and our future. I assumed my friends would have preferred to distract me from my pain rather than make space for it, so I didn't share it. I didn't know how to create space for all of me. As a result, the grief festered and I felt more and more invisible. My grief didn't need to be hidden. What it needed was to be witnessed.

Calling in the Dog
June 2017 – Four Years and Six Months After Second Stroke

I take a breath and paste on my best fake smile. I try to be cheerful and upbeat even as I feel waves of sadness, grief, and anxiety flowing through me. I want my mood to match this beautiful summer day. I'm on vacation in Central Oregon with my daughters. It's the first time I have taken the girls on a trip without their dad. It's the first time I've been on vacation as the lone adult in more than twenty years. I feel incredibly exposed and conspicuous as I travel alone with my young children and feel surprisingly naked without my wedding ring.

Tim and I are officially separated, but we are still living in the same home. He is at home with our dog. Since our house is currently on the market, one of us needs to be there to remove the dog from the house when the realtor has a showing. Tim says he's happy to have quiet time. The cats are being boarded elsewhere and the kids are with me, so I expect Tim is having a pretty low-key week.

The girls and I are currently browsing in a party store. I feel conflicted. My brother died two weeks ago. I am looking for supplies for his Celebration of Life gathering that will be happening in a couple of weeks. Being in this joyful little store feels wrong, somehow disrespectful. Part of me wants to celebrate his life and part of me wants to wear black from head to toe and ban all celebrations from my life for a very long time. I put on my fake smile and carry on, picking up some tie-dyed plates and cups my brother would have loved. I feel myself smile a real smile.

I jump when my phone begins to ring. I'm not surprised to see Tim's name on the screen as he calls often, but I am surprised by the sound of his voice. He is talking fast, sounds out of breath, and seems distressed. I ask him to take a deep breath and tell me *slowly* what is happening.

He keeps talking fast, stuttering his words, telling me that our dog Zoey has gotten loose and is running wild in the cul-de-sac. The realtor is coming soon to show the house and the crazy dog has gotten loose. He says he put the harness on her but doesn't think he buckled it properly and she wiggled out of it. *Damned dog.* He says he can't catch her. Tim is frantic. I feel a rush of adrenalin. I ask him again to take a deep breath and I take one myself as well. Our dog is a pain in the ass when she gets out because she has absolutely no street smarts, she loves everyone, and she just wants to run off and find new friends. He says he's been chasing her and calling her, but she won't come to him.

My daughters are now standing next to me, looking at me with concern in their eyes. I motion for them to head outside. I return the party supplies to the shelf and quickly exit the store. As we walk out into the parking lot toward our car, I ask Tim to put his phone on speaker. I put my phone on speaker as well and start calling for the dog. The girls join in. "Zoey! Here Zoey! Come on, Zoey! Zooooooey!" We are yelling and whistling and calling her name into my phone. It's hilarious. And so very loud. And I am absolutely terrified. I wonder if my heart can truly handle any more of this kind of fear. I silently pray for her safety over and over and over.

Miraculously, after a few minutes of crazy yelling, the dog is caught and harnessed and loaded into Tim's car. Tim sits in the driver's seat of his car as I stand next to mine. I can hear him breathing and I can hear the dog panting. *Damned dog.* He tells me the realtor just drove onto our street. We breathe a collective sigh of relief and end the call. The girls and I sit in the car listening to music for about twenty minutes before I stop shaking enough to drive.

I turn down the music, paste on my fake smile again, and ask the girls what kind of food we should get for lunch. Maybe food will help me decompress a little more from the stress of what just happened.

My cell phone rings again. It's Tim. I feel a little annoyed. *What now?* He says he thinks he injured his head when he was chasing Zoey. I'm confused. I ask if the dog got loose again. He says the dog is safe and in his car. He says he hit his head before. He says he fell while jumping our front fence and then he also bumped his head on a tree branch while trying to grab the dog in our neighbor's yard. I feel the panic rising and force it down. He's on blood thinners. Injuries can be dangerous. I ask him to *slowly* tell me all the details of what happened. I ask him to take a photo of his head and text it to me. I hear my phone beep as the photo comes through. It's hard to tell from the photo if he's okay.

He assures me he is fine. I ask if we should come home. Again, he assures me he is fine. I want to believe him.

I want to paste on my fake smile, move on with my vacation, and have a great time on our first trip without him. Again, he assures me he is fine. I can't seem to shake the waves of sadness, grief, and anxiety flowing through me.

Maybe it's not okay to leave him home alone.

Maybe it's not okay to leave him.

The River of Grief

The unthinkable happens
and I fall headfirst into the river of grief
Flailing, confused, disoriented
Grasping for a lifeline for him and for me

Respite comes with busyness
I get my bearings and slowly move
to the bank of the raging river
I stay busy
It's the only way

Then another unthinkable loss
Oh hell
I fall in again
I'm still busy
It no longer works
Flailing, confused, disoriented
Searching for another way out of this hell of grief

Respite this time comes with change
So I stay busy and work to change everything
to keep the sadness at bay
to keep the rage from spewing out
to keep the despair from taking my life
It works its magic
For a while

The river is strong
Even small losses make me feel crazy now
I withdraw
Isolation helps

Another unthinkable loss
I know the drill
I learn to pretend
I can almost believe I'm okay
Everyone else believes I am

When my marriage ends
I am already busy being busy
Making changes, pretending, and isolating
There's no relief now

Food
Blessed sugar and wheat
Food becomes my way to the shore in the river of hell
I eat to function
I eat to avoid feeling
I eat to keep myself separate and alone
I eat alone in my car
In the dark in my kitchen
When I read, when I write
This soothes and yet simultaneously brings despair
It's not working
nothing really works

Then my brother dies and I just can't
I can't go there
I can't feel
I cling to all the branches
on the banks of that river of grief
I cling like I've never held on before
I can't go there
The house of cards will fall

Oh dear god
What happens if I just stop this insanity?
The fear of drowning is real
The fear of letting go consumes me
The fear of unbearable grief tightens my grip
I can't let go
I have to eat, stay busy, change, isolate, pretend, eat some more

And then one day
yesterday
I woke up
I could clearly see
I am becoming a deep pool of despair
Separate from the river of grief
A new waterway with no way out
I didn't fall in
I wasn't pushed
I created it
It is my own creation
My lifeline has become my noose
I am creating a way to lose the most valuable thing I have—
My self, my soul
They call this complicated grief
I call it hell
Tomato, tomahto

I'm a fighter, a survivor
And today
I'm finding a way to climb out of this pool of unbearable sadness
and I'm walking into the raging river of grief—
To heal.

Separate Vacations
June 2017 – Four Years and Six Months After Second Stroke

It's been about a week since Tim hit his head on a tree branch while trying to catch our dog. He is packing a suitcase, getting ready to fly to Colorado for a week to see his family. The day he flies back to Oregon, I will be flying to California to do a training for a week. We are now ships that pass in the night, each of us literally flying solo.

After the girls and I returned from Central Oregon last week, I told Tim I wanted to keep the house. After recently losing my brother, and knowing we are ending the marriage, losing the house feels like too much. I wasn't sure I could handle one more thing. He agreed. We pulled the house off the market and decided to explore other options. The relief I felt was immense and immediate.

Tim's injuries appear to have healed, but I am still nervous about the bump he sustained on his head and wonder if it's safe for him to fly. I asked him a few days ago to please check with his doctor before making the trip and he agreed. Today he is having a CT scan to make sure he doesn't have any internal bleeding. I am relieved he agreed to take this step.

Thankfully, the results of his CT scan were normal, so our plans move forward as scheduled. My mother will spend the week with Tim and the kids while I'm in California, making sure that he has breaks and doesn't get too overwhelmed. I can see that we are starting to get a little taste of living separately, learning to work as a team in a very different way.

Two weeks later...

Tim's trip to Colorado went smoothly, and I am now in California finishing up a training. I've been here for almost a week and will fly home tomorrow. It's been good for me to look forward and start planning for my future, planning for the day when I will return to working outside of the home.

It's still early morning and I am planning to meet some colleagues for breakfast soon. I've been up for a couple of hours, enjoying the quiet and the time alone. I left the drapes open a little last night so the blackout curtains wouldn't confuse my body into thinking it was still nighttime. I want to take advantage of the peace and quiet when I have the chance.

I am startled when my phone rings. It's Tim. I answer and the second he starts speaking, I know something is wrong. He says he's "not right," says he can't see clearly, and his hand-eye coordination is off. I ask him to get my mom and put her on the phone. I hear the confusion in her voice as she says hello. I calmly and sternly tell her to call 911, *"Right now!"* She agrees. I hang up and call my best friend who lives a mile away from my home and ask her to please meet the ambulance at my house so I can speak directly with the paramedics when they get there. I don't know what is happening, but I do know Tim's medical history and I know I can relay that information quickly and succinctly.

My friend calls me back a few minutes later and I relay the medical history to a paramedic. Tim is taken by ambulance to the nearest hospital. My mom stays at the house with the girls and my friend heads to the hospital. It's all very smooth and efficient.

I hang up and call the airline and ask to switch my flight from tomorrow to today. I then call the car service and ask for a shuttle to the airport. A car will be here in an hour. I call the front desk and they agree to allow for an early checkout without penalty. I pack up my belongings and head to the lobby to check out. I find a colleague from my breakfast group and share the news. I am in full-on crisis management mode and don't let myself feel anything until I am sitting in the back of the town car on the way to the airport. I sit in the car, quietly weeping as the waves of fear flow through me.

I say prayer after prayer after prayer for Tim.

I am not ready to fly solo.

Limbo

August 2017 – Four Years and Eight Months After Second Stroke

Sometimes I think Tim has the worst luck in the world and sometimes I am amazed by the miracles that continually happen for him. Yesterday, he had surgery to drain a very large subdural hematoma, a bleed that happens between the brain and the skull. The surgery went incredibly well. Before surgery, he didn't have the ability to move his right arm or right leg and today, only one day later, he is up and walking around. I never cease to be astounded by what modern medicine can do. Tim has some healing time in front of him, has a nickel-sized hole in his skull and two drains in his scalp, but he is blessed with access to excellent medical care and is expected to fully recover from this latest setback.

Evidently, he *did* get a brain bleed after bumping his head on the tree branch while chasing our dog. It was a slow bleed that wasn't detectable on a CT scan a week after the injury and didn't start causing detectable problems until thirty days later. Because he takes blood thinners for his blood-clotting disorder, he is at risk of internal bleeding following any injury. The bleed eventually led to symptoms similar to those he experienced with his two large strokes, including speech challenges and paralysis on the right side of his body.

Tim and I are in a strange space. We are living together, and yet we are separated and moving toward divorce. *Limbo*. He's not able to work. I want to return to working but don't know how that will play out, given his needs and the needs of our children. *Limbo*. We both want to do what's best for the kids. We also want to do what's best for ourselves. We want to be happy again. He will be in the hospital for a while. He needs my care right now, which leaves me feeling trapped in our situation, unable to take steps to move forward. *More limbo.* I feel guilty for feeling this way. I signed up for this. I took vows.

Maybe it's me who has the worst luck in the world.

Arms of Hope

Standing on a fault line
one foot in my old way of being
one foot in the new
my world is shaking
I no longer can stay
in this space
I am fully aware
I know I have to choose

Will I choose fear
and fall back
keeping myself "safe"
and unspeakably lonely
or will I choose faith
in my true self
and fall
into the unknown
into the beautiful
arms of hope

PART THREE

Calm Seas

The only real security is not in owning or possessing,
not in demanding or expecting,
not in hoping, even. Security in a relationship lies
neither in looking back
to what it was in nostalgia, nor forward
to what it might be in dread or anticipation,
but living in the present relationship and
accepting it as it is now.

— Anne Morrow Lindbergh

Uncoupling
November 2018 – Ten Years and Ten Months After First Stroke

Tim and I are dressed in our finest casual clothing. It's a beautiful fall day and we are standing in a cozy hotel room at one of our favorite resorts at the beach. Even though there are only a handful of people at this gathering, the energy in the room radiates big excitement and lots of love. I am surprisingly nervous. The nerves are familiar—taking me back to those wedding day jitters all those years ago. This isn't a wedding though. It's a ceremony to honor the beginning, middle, *and ending* of our marriage.

It's been more than a decade since the first stroke and a lot of things have changed. Today we are formally reciting new, more appropriate vows. We are here to honor our uncoupling process and publicly state our new agreements to each other in the presence of our children and a couple of dear friends.

Vowing to be friends, co-parents, family.

Letting go of spouse, husband, wife.

We stand here listening to some of the same words spoken on our wedding day. I find it interesting that words spoken in a wedding ceremony are also applicable in an uncoupling. I breathe in the beautiful words and connect to their meaning in a new way. I am reminded of these words of Kahlil Gibran—also spoken in our wedding ceremony—"Love one another, but make not a bond of love; Let it rather be a moving sea between the shores of your souls." These words bring a deep sense of relief and I find myself breathing out blessings of hope to Tim, to my daughters, and to myself. We are finding a new way to love one another.

We stand here, holding hands, looking into each other's eyes with love, kindness, and the pride that only comes with having done something *really well*.

I feel the tears flowing down my cheeks as our eight-year-old daughters sing a song about sanctuary to bring the ceremony to a close.

Such a magical moment.

Although our legal divorce didn't come until many months later, it was that beautiful ceremony that truly marked the ending of our marriage and supported us in moving forward with commitment to ourselves, our children, and each other in a uniquely kind and loving way. I discovered that relationships can move through healthy changes. I learned that a marriage can end in a way that allows children to remain deeply connected to both parents.

Shocking Divorce Statistics
November 2018 – Ten Years and Ten Months After First Stroke

I stare out at the beautiful Pacific Ocean from the balcony of my hotel room. The kids are down on the beach with Tim and I am taking a few minutes alone to breathe and listen and fill my proverbial cup. As I close my eyes and listen to the sound of the waves, I find myself reflecting on marriage and divorce and the journey we've been on for the past decade since Tim's first stroke. We had our uncoupling ceremony yesterday and today I feel more at peace than I have in a very long time.

Years ago, not too long after Tim's first stroke, I heard that about 70 percent of married couples in which one spouse has aphasia end up getting divorced. While that number is quite astounding and may or may not be true, it shocked me at the time. Today it doesn't surprise me at all. What does surprise me is the wave of compassion I have for those in the 30 percent of marriages who stay together. My heart goes out to all of them. I wonder what makes them stay. I wonder if they are comfortably numb or living happily ever after. I wonder if they are like me and wrestling with the decision of whether to stay or go. Like me, maybe they stay because they gave their word.

I wonder how many of those 30 percent are resigned to a life of sacrifice, not knowing there is another option, an option that may leave everyone better off than they were before.

I used to believe divorce was the worst choice. Now I believe it may be one of the most humane acts in the midst of something unbearable. Now I believe divorce can be a path to peace.

One Day

One day
you will find yourself
walking down
an unknown road

It isn't pretty
it isn't paved in gold
it isn't somewhere
you've ever been before

On this road
you will know
you are walking away
from your old life

Part of you wants
to go back
part of you wants
to keep walking

Turn off the voices
in your head
listen to that whisper
in your heart

Just listen because
in that whisper
you will hear your truth
the truth to guide you on

Listen to that whisper
honor your inner knowing
it will lead you
back to yourself

Family Matters
March 2019 – Eleven Years and Two Months After First Stroke

I never imagined things would be this good again. It's a lovely evening and our family is having dinner at one of our favorite restaurants in a beautiful little beach town on the Oregon Coast. It's spring break and this year Tim and I decided to go on a family vacation.

Tim and I are separated—we've been living apart for more than a year but still gather frequently for meals, outings, and our daughters' school events. Spending part of spring break together with our kids is aligned with the way we are choosing to define our family. Our definition of family is not determined by marriage or divorce but more by the love and kindness that exists between us. This works for us.

Since I often carry playing cards with me when we travel or go to restaurants, we are all enjoying a rousing game of Crazy Eights as we wait for our food. The smiles, the laughter, and the delight that radiate from our children are infectious and my heart swells with joy. It now makes sense that happiness isn't a destination but rather is something that you feel in the moments along the way.

I realize that after all this time and after all the upheaval in our marriage, I am happy—truly happy in this moment with this beautiful little family I am blessed to call mine.

When Leaving Makes It Better
October 2019 – Eleven Years and Nine Months After First Stroke

When I got the call, I didn't hesitate at all when saying the girls and I would go to Colorado. Tim's dad, who is my father-in-law and my daughters' grandfather, passed away a few weeks ago and we are here to attend his memorial service and to provide comfort to Tim, his mom, and to the rest of the family in this sad time. Tim was able to come out here a few weeks before his dad died. It was such a blessing he was able to spend those final weeks with his dad and be supportive to his mom during that time. I am so grateful we are all able to be here today.

It's a cold and sunny fall day in Loveland, Colorado, and we are gathered at the home of Tim's parents. Our daughters and I arrived in town last night and after spending the night in a hotel, we are meeting up with the family today. Tim and I have been separated for three years and though we aren't yet legally divorced, we are definitely no longer married.

Even though our separation and the intention to leave our marriage was not well-accepted by his family at first, things have changed over time. Tim and I continued to show up as a family and live from our values and, surprisingly, the people around us got on board. We are still a family—our structure just looks a little different.

Today we are packed in a room with lots of people—some telling stories, some looking at photo albums, all listening to the sounds of little ones in the room laughing and playing. The sounds of family. The sounds of love. I am deeply saddened by the passing of my father-in-law. He was a good man who loved his family dearly. I am saddened by the hole his passing leaves in my mother-in-law's life after more than six decades of marriage. Their love for each other was always so present. His leaving has left her devastated. Her grief today is palpable and raw.

Some leavings, like the ending of a marriage, can make things better.

Some leavings, like the death of a loved one, can result in unbearable grief.

Maybe loving and leaving are inextricable.

Family Sundays
November 2019 – Eleven Years and Ten Months After the First Stroke

It's a strange and typical Sunday morning for our family. It's a lovely autumn day and Tim and I and our daughters are sitting in the sanctuary of our Unitarian Universalist church. After the opening words, I watch with misty eyes as our daughters go to the front of the room for a story. As the children leave for their religious education classes (aka Sunday School), the adults in the congregation stand and sing. It's all very sweet. Tim and I smile at each other and sit back down, listening to the music and welcoming whatever wisdom may come our way. It's surprisingly pleasant.

I started attending this church about a year ago with a friend and then, shortly after that, I started bringing our daughters each week. I wanted a place that felt spiritual but not religious—a place that would provide our children some education about religions of all kinds in a way that preached tolerance rather than one right way of thinking. The principles of the Unitarian Universalist church were very much in alignment with my beliefs. The principles were also in alignment with the way that Tim and I were committed to raising our children.

A few months after the girls and I started going to church, Tim asked if he could join us as well. I was open to it and, over time, Sundays became the day for our family. He would drive to our home in the morning and then I would drive us all across town to church. We would sit together, attend coffee hour after the service, and then we would all go out to lunch after that. Having a meal together once a week became a fun way to discuss what we had learned in church and connect as a family unit. It became a way for the girls to see Tim and me interacting as friends.

Sunday church-and-lunch has become a ritual, a ritual that doesn't require me and Tim to be married, a ritual that breathes healing back into our fractured family.

Divorce
April 2020 – Twelve Years and Three Months After First Stroke

We are in my home office getting legally divorced on a Zoom call. It's strange because it feels like any other day. It's a beautiful spring day. Some might chuckle and say it's a good day for a divorce. Tim and I are sitting side by side watching the judge on a computer screen. I am reminded of the big reveal in *The Wizard of Oz*. The divorce proceeding seems really big and mysterious and then, when it's finally here, it's not that big a deal. I expect to feel sad or relieved or something after the process is done and yet all I really feel is normal.

We are in the beginning of a global pandemic, so we are doing this divorce thing virtually, which seems rather strange, but it's all very civilized and banal. Since having our formal uncoupling ceremony about eighteen months ago, this mostly feels like one last hoop we're jumping through, a legal formality. In my heart of hearts, our true divorce already happened.

It's interesting to me that Tim and I dated for four years before marrying and then, in similar fashion, we were separated for four years before divorcing. Evidently, we don't rush into things and we don't rush out of them either. That brings me solace. Even though this post-stroke journey over the past twelve years was challenging, to say the least, we gave it a go, we gave it our best shot. We rose to the occasion and walked through the hard times, choosing to find a way through it all that would benefit our children, not leave them carrying extra baggage.

Maybe our story didn't turn out to be *happily ever after.*

But then again, maybe it did.

Freedom

There are times in life
when connections
become
the ties that bind

So we sever the ties
Gather the threads
and weave
the fabric of freedom

Epilogue

When I was young in the sixties and seventies, I was taught to believe that little girls grow up to be married. What I learned from books and the culture around me was that marriage would look one of two ways.

The first way for a girl to be married was to be a princess. You would meet your Prince Charming and be swept off your feet and live happily ever after without ever getting pregnant or fat or sick or old. I read many stories about this scenario but didn't know anyone personally who experienced that kind of life. It was something to dream about and desire, like winning a million dollars or living in a house like the one on *The Brady Bunch*, but I figured the likelihood of Prince Charming swooping in was pretty low.

The second way for a girl to be married was to be a servant. You get married and become a housewife and are responsible for the care of your children, your spouse, your spouse's parents, your pets, your home, and all things domestic. You might also have a part-time job on the side to help make ends meet. I watched my mother and all the moms of my friends take on the servant role in their marriages and that option seemed rather bleak.

As a young girl, I was primed for the role of the servant wife. As the oldest daughter, somehow it was even more my duty to learn the role. I learned to listen to my parents, especially my dad, and I did what I was told. Listening to my own voice and doing what I desired often resulted in *consequences*. I had chores that were consistent with "women's work," including washing dishes, doing laundry, and cleaning house. I learned to take care of the garden and our pets.

Relaxing with a book was seen as lazy, so I took to reading books with a flashlight at night in my bed. I was charged with looking after my little sister, even when I would have rather been alone with my friends. I took 4-H classes in cooking and sewing. I wore pretty dresses. I took piano lessons. I learned to model clothing I made myself.

When my grandfather came to live with us, I took on even more, as my mom had the added responsibility of being my grandpa's primary caregiver. I babysat, even when I didn't want to. I worked in restaurants. I worked as a maid in several hotels. I had to go to school as a child, but academics were not a priority beyond the basics. College wasn't discussed or encouraged. It was never clear how a girl like me could acquire a career.

I got really good at being good, most of the time. I learned to tamp down my natural exuberance and stifle my creativity so I could blend in and please my parents, my teachers, and my elders. The idea that I would fall in love with some guy, be swept off my feet and taken away into a beautiful life full of love and riches and joy, became a joke to me. I became pretty jaded about it, believing that if I did fall madly in love with some handsome prince and got married, I would still probably end up being the servant wife. It was not appealing and I stayed the hell away from commitment for a long, long time.

When I met Tim in my early thirties, I started to believe that the definition of marriage and my role in it could be expanded. I was able to see that he could have his career and I could have one too. I could see that we could travel and have fun and share the responsibilities in our home. It was a very new idea for me. After four years of dating, we married. When we decided to start a family, I believed we could probably do that differently as well. I was going to stay home with the kids until they went to school and then I was going to go back to work. I was not exactly a princess, but I was most definitely not a servant wife.

My husband's first stroke threw a wrench into everything. In one mighty moment, I lost my pseudo-princess role and was thrown into the servant role, because service is what caregivers do. I wasn't prepared. The storyline was just too different.

As I often do, I looked to books and stories for guidance. The few stories I found written by wives of stroke survivors all told the same story of "standing by your man." It was disheartening. I didn't have a roadmap. All I could envision was life as a caregiver in the same way it played out with my mom. She wasn't happy as the proverbial servant wife.

Fortunately, as Tim recovered from the first stroke, we found our way back to equilibrium in our roles as husband and wife. Our relationship moved back into being a partnership and I was so relieved.

When the second stroke happened, I was thrown back into the caregiver role—that time with a couple of two-year-old daughters in addition to my husband. The pseudo-princess role was nowhere to be found. There was no partnership. It was just me, taking care of them, all of them. I was officially the servant wife. I pretended for a long time that things were good, or at least sort of okay. Eventually, I didn't want to keep pretending things were good. I didn't want to keep pretending that I was *being good*. I was tired of being good.

In the years following Tim's strokes, people would often say to me, "I don't know how you do all that you do," and I would smile and thank them, as if it were a compliment of some sort. The truth is I didn't believe I had a choice. It was my role to suck it up and do what had to be done. I didn't know there was any other option. To my mind, when my husband became disabled, being the caregiver was my only choice. I had to set aside my own feelings and needs and take on that role. It worked for a while, and then things got so bad that I started losing touch with my humanity, losing touch with those parts of me that I deemed most precious.

As I lost touch with my innermost self, everything started to unravel and the tension at home became unbearable. Therapy, coaching, writing, listening to my inner guides more than I listened to the narratives in our culture, and finding my own voice, and expressing it all became my pathways back to myself. I learned to listen to my body and my emotions and that deep inner knowing that told me I am not here to live in misery. I found that I didn't need a prince to come in and save me. I learned to save myself. I became my own Royal Highness.

Through trial and error and lots of outside support, I learned to expand my definition of a caregiver. I learned it doesn't have to be a sacrificial relationship. I don't have to disappear myself in order to care for another. I learned it can be different.

Because Tim and I didn't have a roadmap for exactly what we were doing, we forged ahead and created our own path. We found a way to co-exist that worked for each of us, for both of us, and for our kids. We found a way to make each of us a priority without leaving anyone behind. We found a way to ensure that we all mattered.

Now, as we move forward as a nontraditional family, as we co-parent, support one another, and care deeply about each other and our kids, it is my hope to create something that might inspire others to maintain some hope in the face of difficult times. Your life may not end up looking anything like you had imagined, but that doesn't mean it won't be wonderful.

Even though Tim and I made the loving decision to divorce and not spend the rest of our lives together as a married couple, the intention to be connected still exists. We have children together. We are good friends. We care deeply about our family and each other.

Years ago, standing on a beach on the island of St. Thomas during our wedding ceremony, we listened as our wedding officiant recited the following words by Anne Morrow Lindbergh. They are as relevant today as they were back then.

"For relationships, too, must be like islands, one must accept them for what they are here and now, within their limits—islands, surrounded and interrupted by the sea, and continually visited and abandoned by

the tides. One must accept the security of the winged life, of the ebb and flow, of intermittency."

As I look back on all that's happened, I can clearly see that what started as a romantic love story ended up being a transformative story of deep and compassionate love.

We *are* connected.

We *are* happy.

We *are* living our happily-ever-after story.

May you find your happily-ever-after story as well.

Family Photo, November 2012 – Two Weeks Before Second Stroke

Acknowledgments

Even though it was challenging to live this story and then write about it, seeing this book in print is truly a dream come true and it makes my little writer heart so freaking happy. I am grateful for all the people who supported and loved me through the tough times, and for all those who cheered me on and encouraged me as I endeavored to tell my story.

My gratitude is twofold. First is the gratitude I feel for all the love, kindness, and support Tim and I received as we lived this story. Second is the gratitude I feel for all the love, kindness, and support I received as I took this big vulnerable step of sharing my writing with the world. I am hopeful the acknowledgments below will show my appreciation for both camps.

First and foremost, I am so grateful to **Tim** for loving me. Even though our journey was both beautiful and horrible, I am truly thankful I got to walk it with him. I am also grateful to him for being supportive of my writing and for being open to my sharing of this complicated and painful story. I am grateful to **my daughters, Lienne and Malaya**, for bringing more light into my life than I ever dreamed possible. My love for them is immeasurable, bigger than the moon, filling the entire Universe with sparkly light.

I am grateful to **my mom** for teaching me that when you know better, you do better. I have tried to weave that message into everything throughout my life. I am grateful to **my dad** for teaching me how to get things done, even the hard things in hard times. I am learning to honor his ways and weave in some new, more kind and loving ways as well.

I am grateful to **my sister Linda** for loving me and for her commitment to keep moving forward when challenges come up. She and I share a deeply held desire to do good in this world. I will always be cheering her on. I am grateful to **my brother Steve** for never letting me take myself or life too seriously. I will never forget all the times he just showed up and helped me do things around the house when Tim was hospitalized or recovering. I hope he knows the impact he had on my life. I am grateful to **Leo and Velma** for raising a child into a good and kind man.

There are many who cared for me so I, in turn, could care for Tim and our daughters. Of those, I am especially grateful to **Leili** for being an amazing friend, evolutionary partner, and god-sister. I am so thankful for her willingness to drop everything and show up when I needed her, time after time after time. The experience of feeling held in my darkest moments is something I endeavor to repay her in this lifetime. I am deeply grateful to **Chris R. and Helen** for jumping on a plane, cutting short their vacation, and showing up at the hospital when they heard the news of Tim's first stroke. I am extremely grateful to **Monte and Kristy** for sticking with Tim and our family through thick and thin. Their loyalty has been a godsend. I am grateful to **Michelle C. and her family** for being there for us in some of our darkest hours. I am grateful to **Margaret, Chrissy, Trish, René, and Lynne** for decades of friendship, support, and laughter. I am thankful to **Geoff and Heidi** for their ongoing love and support.

I am grateful to **Beth, Marilyn, Paula, and Jenn** for being the best sacred soul-sisters ever. I am grateful to **Noelle and Heather** for truly seeing me and always inspiring me to grow.

I am extremely grateful to **Rick J.** for encouraging my authentic Self to step forward so she could start leading my beautiful life. I appreciate **Tracy D.** for metaphorically holding my hand through one of the toughest transitions of my life. I am so thankful to **Marianne M.** for listening to me with compassion week after week while caring for my cats and dog. I am grateful to **Ashlea, Kirstin, Suzie, Maureen, Erin, Stephanie, Mia, and Gail** for their sisterhood that started on our Wayfinder journey. I am grateful to **Katherine Woodward Thomas** for creating the Conscious

Uncoupling™ process and for giving us (and the world) the language to end a marriage *well*.

I am eternally grateful to **Dr. Stanley Barnwell** for getting the blood clot on the first try. I know it saved Tim's life. I am so grateful to **Dr. Michael Carroll** for being an amazing primary care physician who always treated Tim with respect, allowing him to maintain his dignity.

I want to sincerely thank **Sully** for encouraging me to honor my love of writing and for igniting the spark that grew into the intention for this book. I am grateful to **Mary B.** for decades of friendship and for encouraging me to "just write the damned book." I am grateful to **Chrissa, Ashley, Tiffany, Nicole, and Havilah** for their shared love of reading and for not thinking I was crazy to want to write a book. I am thankful to **Sulima, Kay, Steph, Char, and Yvonne** for listening to me read stories from this book with open minds and open hearts. Their feedback was always helpful and kind. I am grateful for **Sarah and Inger and the writing community** for their ongoing support that created a safe space so I could finish this project instead of shelving it. I am deeply grateful to **Isaac, Thorald, Kristen, Andi, Debbie, Jade, Vanessa, Gianna, Jillian, Karal, and Justin** for so lovingly encouraging me to use my voice.

Even though the following are not named individually, the love and gratitude I feel for them is enormous. I am grateful for the **paramedics, firefighters, ambulance drivers, nurses, doctors, technicians, and all the supporting medical personnel** for all they do to help those in need. Their work matters. I am grateful to **speech language pathologists, psychotherapists, physical therapists, and occupational therapists** for being in the business of restoring dignity. I am so thankful for **support groups** for allowing safe spaces to be human. I am grateful to the **security guard** at Tim's place of employment for helping him after the second stroke. My gratitude goes out to all the **friends and family** who visited at the hospital, brought us meals, gave rides to Tim, called and sent cards, texts, emails, and letters. What a wonderful village of circling wagons. My cup runneth over.

Reading Group Guide
Questions for Discussion or Self-Reflection

What do you think motivated the author to share her story?

How might you be seeing the marriages of your grandparents and/or parents in a new or different way after reading this book?

How might you be seeing your own marriage or relationship in a new or different way after reading this book?

What did you think of the author's voice or style?

What story or scene has stuck with you the most?

If you could ask the author anything, what would it be? (Please feel free to share your questions with the author at www. devonervin.com or write to hello@devonervin.com.)

What were your beliefs about the roles of wives when you were growing up? Were the narratives of the Princess Wife and the Servant Wife similar to what you learned?

What actions might you take if you have a friend or family member who reluctantly becomes a caregiver?

In therapy, Devon discovered her husband wasn't being an asshole, but rather was really struggling with deficits brought on by the two strokes. Were there times in your life when you discovered something you absolutely knew to be true was, in fact, not? How did you handle the shift in knowing?

How does discovering one's voice (Tim's and/or Devon's) contribute to a better ending in this story?

How has your perspective on divorce changed (or not) after reading these stories?

What similar caregiver journeys have you been on in your own life? What would you do differently today?

What feelings came up that surprised you?

How do these stories inspire you to look at things in your own life in a different way?

What creative endeavors bring healing to your life? Writing? Drawing? Painting? Singing? Songwriting? Playing music? Dancing? Gardening? Something else?

How connected do you feel in the world?

How might you go about creating your own village of support?

What article of clothing do you own (or previously owned) that is inextricably tied to a painful memory? What is the clothing's story?

About the Author

Devon Ervin is a writer and certified life coach who specializes in making sure we are all seen and heard. She has a passion for writing poetry and stories that heal. Devon is committed to using words, both spoken and written, to build connections, promote healing, and encourage tapping into creativity. When she's not coaching or writing, you can find her spending time with family or friends or reading a good book. Devon lives in Oregon with her daughters and several pets. *The Reluctant Caregiver* is her first book.

For more information, visit her website at www.devonervin.com.

Index

Printed in the USA
CPSIA information can be obtained
at www.ICGtesting.com
LVHW051549170923
758448LV00013B/1073

9 798987 920336